HAMLYN BIRD BEHAVIOUR GUIDES

WILDFOWL

HAMLYN BIRD BEHAVIOUR GUIDES

WILDFOWL

MALCOLM OGILVIE

BRUCE PEARSON

HAMLYN

TITLE PAGE ILLUSTRATION *A Canada Goose bathes with utmost vigour, splashing and shuffling the water up with its wings and rolling right over on its back. It erects the feathers all over its body so that the water can penetrate as far as possible (see page 115).*

First published in 1994 by Hamlyn Limited,
an imprint of Reed Consumer Books Ltd
Michelin House, 81 Fulham Road, London SW3 6RB
and Auckland, Melbourne, Singapore and Toronto

Copyright © Reed International Books Limited 1994

Text copyright © Malcolm Ogilvie 1994
Illustrations copyright © Bruce Pearson 1994
Map copyright © Reed International Books Limited 1994

ISBN 0 600 57973 5

A CIP catalogue record for this book is available from the British Library

Page design by Sue Michniewicz
Map by Louise Griffiths

Printed in China

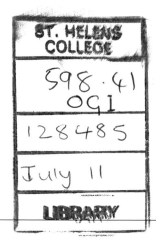

Contents

INTRODUCTION

The family of wildfowl comprises the swans, the geese and the ducks, of which, worldwide, there are about 140 different species. Of these, 52 occur in Britain (three swans, ten geese and 38 ducks). However, three of the goose species and 15 of the ducks are only vagrants, perhaps occurring annually in very small numbers but most much more rarely than that.

The wildfowl are all waterbirds with webbed feet and are therefore good swimmers and, in some cases, divers, although several species feed on land and are well capable of walking and running. All the British species are strong flyers, and many undertake long-distance migrations between their breeding and wintering ground every autumn and spring.

The most obvious physical characteristic which distinguishes wildfowl from all other birds is the bill. Although there is great variation in size and shape, which relates to adaptations to enable the different species to feed on different foods, the basic structure is the same whether it is over 100 mm long, like that of the Whooper Swan, or under 30 mm, as the bills of Long-tailed and Harlequin Ducks. It is covered with a thin layer of skin and has, at its tip, a horny plate called the 'nail', after its similarity to a fingernail. The sides of both upper and lower mandibles are serrated for the better grasping of food items.

Several internal details of musculature and skeleton are shared by all the wildfowl, while externally they are noted for the thickness of their plumage. Their feathers overlie a dense layer of down which helps provide necessary insulation against the cold water. The down is also used as a nest lining by the majority of species, being plucked by the female from her breast area.

The wildfowl are classified as a family, the Anatidae, which is divided first into two subfamilies, the Anserinae (the swans and geese) and the Anatinae (the ducks), and then into tribes. This is merely a convenient way of grouping species which appear to be closely related, and tribe names are rarely used in other than major scientific reference works.

The swans and geese, despite very considerable size differences, are closely related. Males and females are identical in plumage, although the male is a little larger. The three swans include the resident Mute and the winter-visiting Whooper and Bewick's. Of the ten goose species, the Greylag and the introduced Canada

A female Mallard feigns injury to draw a predator away from her nest or brood. This 'broken-wing' display is very effective at fooling foxes or dogs which pursue what they think is easy prey as the duck thrashes the water with its wings and calls loudly (see pages 107–8).

breed, while the Bean, Pink-footed, White-fronted, Barnacle and Brent all winter in Britain, and the Lesser White-fronted, Snow and Red-breasted Geese are vagrants.

The next group, the shelducks and sheldgeese, includes the Common Shelduck, which breeds in Britain, as does the introduced Egyptian Goose. The third species, the Ruddy Shelduck, is a rare vagrant. Male and female Egyptian Goose have similar plumage, but there are slight sexual differences in the two shelducks. The birds in this group have more flattened bills than the geese and share the characteristics of large white patches on their wings as well as an iridescent 'speculum', a coloured panel towards the rear of the wing, typical of many ducks.

Two further introduced species, the Mandarin Duck and the Wood Duck, are described as perching ducks. They frequently do

perch, on branches, and they also nest in tree holes. The males are very brightly patterned, but the females are much duller.

Eleven species of dabbling ducks occur in Britain of which seven regularly breed and/or winter: Wigeon, Gadwall, Teal, Mallard, Pintail, Garganey and Shoveler. American Wigeon, Baikal Teal, Black Duck and Blue-winged Teal are vagrants. Their legs are placed near the centre of the body, giving them a horizontal stance on land, and their bills are rather broad and flattened. The males are brightly plumaged, the females a well-camouflaged brown, which protects them when nesting

Diving ducks are well adapted to feeding underwater, with their legs set well back on their bodies. They have rounded, heavy bodies and take off only after a splashing run. Pochard, Tufted Duck and Scaup breed and/or winter here, while the vagrant Red-crested Pochard, Ring-necked Duck and Ferruginous Duck bring the tally of species to six. The sexes are different in plumage but none are brightly coloured.

The Common Eider is the sole resident representative of the eider tribe, the King Eider and Steller's Eider occurring as vagrants. Their bodies are thickset and they are competent divers. The males are boldly patterned with black and white, the females superbly camouflaged in browns.

The seaduck group embraces twelve species, of which Long-tailed Duck, Common and Velvet Scoters, Goldeneye, Smew, Red-breasted Merganser and Goosander are all regular breeders or visitors, while Harlequin Duck, Surf Scoter, Bufflehead, Barrow's Goldeneye and Hooded Merganser are vagrants. These are marine ducks, all of them good divers but awkward movers on land. Most of the males are predominantly black and white, the females mainly brown or grey and white.

The final group of wildfowl is the stifftails, of which there is just the introduced North American Ruddy Duck in Britain although the White-headed Duck may have occurred a couple of times as a vagrant. They are small with stout bodies, low in the water, and are accomplished divers. The sexes are different but neither has bright plumage.

A party of White-fronted Geese 'whiffles' down out of the sky. Whiffling is the name given to the side-slipping undertaken by geese when they wish to lose height rapidly, as when dropping steeply into a roost. The term itself probably comes from the rushing sound of the wings through the air. During their tumbling birds will even turn on their backs, although their head will remain the right way up. This may be important, as it is with pilots, in keeping a track of the true horizontal.

FEEDING BEHAVIOUR AND HABITS

The majority of birds spend a large part of every day seeking food, apart from some birds of prey which, if they are successful in hunting their prey, can gorge themselves at a single meal and then go many hours or even a day or two without needing to feed again. Wildfowl belong in the former category. The commonest activities which wildfowl will be seen performing are, therefore, those associated with feeding. These may include feeding while swimming, up-ending, diving, feeding on exposed mudflats or grazing on dry land.

The manner in which different species move on water or land and the ways in which they obtain their food can be completely specific or, at the least, can help to narrow the identification down to a small group of species. This can be true in circumstances where the plumage detail necessary for identification may not be sufficiently visible. Silhouettes of wildfowl, especially on the water, can be very revealing.

As will have been apparent from what I said in the introduction, wildfowl can be divided into three main types based on their principal feeding behaviour. Firstly, there are those species, mainly swans and dabbling ducks, which feed predominantly from the surface of the water, or if from below the surface then doing so without diving, e.g., by dipping their head and neck beneath the water or by up-ending. Secondly, there are the underwater feeders such as the diving ducks, eiders, seaducks and stifftails. These submerge completely in order to find their food, although the depths to which they go and the length of time which they spend under water vary greatly. Finally, there are those species, particularly the geese, which feed mainly on

When wildfowl swim, they float in a number of different ways, their silhouette giving important identification clues even when plumage details cannot be seen. Here, as examples, are, from the top: King Eider (male in eclipse plumage) low on the water, tail flat on the surface; Bewick's Swan, long, body; short and rounded tail held clear of surface, upright neck; Scaup, broad and rounded body, short neck, tail flat; Brent Goose, buoyant, tail high; White-headed Duck, rounded, dumpy body, very short neck; Velvet Scoter, long and low, tail down though cocked in display; Ferruginous Duck, rounded back; Gadwall, flat back, longer neck, tail up.

land or, in the case of the shelducks, on areas of coastal and estuarine mud and sand flats which are exposed by the tide.

It should not be thought that these feeding methods are mutually exclusive. Virtually all the dabbling ducks can and do dive for food where it is abundant, although most do so only rarely. The food source has to be a particularly good one because these ducks, not really built for diving, use a lot of energy getting below the surface. Equally, the majority of diving ducks will feed from the surface in circumstances where suitable food is readily available to them. Geese, too, although feeding on land most of the time, may up-end in shallow water to reach submerged aquatic vegetation. Swans can frequently be seen feeding on dry land, particularly on agricultural land. This exploitation of grass and other crops on farmland is a fairly recent adaptation, and the proportion of food obtained in this way by all three species compared with feeding in water by surface-feeding and up-ending has increased considerably in recent years.

SWIMMING AND FEEDING FROM THE SURFACE

When the three species of swans are swimming their backs are slightly domed, sloping down to the front, where the neck joins the body, and down towards the tail. The silhouette of the **Mute Swan**, however, differs markedly from those of the **Whooper Swan** and the smaller **Bewick's**, because most adult Mutes hold their wings slightly raised from their body, giving them a much more bulky appearance. They generally hold their longer tail cocked up from the water, which the other two species rarely do. Again, the Whooper and Bewick's Swans tend to hold their necks perpendicular to the water surface and their heads and bills more or less parallel to it, while the Mute Swan's neck is held in a sinuous curve with the head and bill pointing slightly downwards. These are the normal attitudes for these species, but in certain circumstances Mute Swans may hold their necks straight up, particularly when alarmed or when swimming quickly. The tail of the Mute Swan is much longer and more pointed than that of the Whooper or Bewick's, and this can often be detected at considerable distances. It is also very apparent when the birds are up-ending (*see* below).

Although geese spend more time on land and less time on the water than any other wildfowl, when they do swim they ride high in the water with their tails cocked up at an angle of about 45 degrees. This shows off the distinctive white undertail-coverts common to all species. The back of a goose is domed, sloping both to the front and to the tail, but in practice the closed wings bridge the gap between the low point where the neck joins the body and the cocked-up tail, so that the overall effect is of a slight upward slope from front to back. The only exception to this is the **Brent Goose**, in which the line is more or less horizontal. The shelducks and the **Egyptian Goose** also have more horizontal backs.

Dabbling ducks, like the geese, swim buoyantly and with their tails cocked up off the water, but all exhibit a nearly horizontal back. In a side-on position, there are some differences which help to identify certain species. For example, there is the long, thin neck of the **Pintail**, together with its long pointed tail, obvious in the female even without the tail streamers of the male. There is also the completely distinctive heavy head and large bill of the **Shoveler** which is rarely lifted far from the water's surface, whether or not the bird is feeding; the effect is to make it appear as if the whole bird is swimming quite low in the water.

The remaining common dabbling ducks are best distinguished by size, if the plumage details cannot be seen, but it is worth bearing in mind that the neck length of the **Wigeon** and **Teal** appears shorter in proportion to overall size than it does in the **Gadwall** and **Mallard**. There is probably less difference in actual measurements than this appearance suggests; it is rather a function of the way the birds hold themselves, whether the neck is stretched or hunched down.

The introduced **Mandarin Duck** holds itself rather like a dabbling duck, but the adult male's extraordinary 'sails' completely alter the silhouette to something quite unlike any other species. The female is very like a dabbling duck.

All the other kinds of ducks, which feed principally by diving, also swim comparatively low in the water and have relatively short tails which are only occasionally lifted clear of the surface. The two common freshwater species, the **Tufted Duck** and the **Pochard**, can readily be told apart on silhouette, the former having a more horizontal, less rounded, back and a short, stubby tail which is more often held out of the water.

The eiders and most of the seaducks, notably the **Goldeneye**, have well-domed backs. The long tail streamers of the male **Long-tailed Duck** are held clear of the water but should not cause this species to be confused with a **Pintail**, which has a much longer neck. The female Longtail keeps its tail flat on the surface most of the time. This is true, too, of the scoters, in which a raised tail is usually a sign that the birds are displaying to each other. Their silhouette is then noticeably different.

13

The **Red-breasted Merganser** and **Goosander**, being rather longer in the body than other ducks, give the appearance of having more horizontal backs, although they, too, are actually slightly dome-backed. Their long, flat heads and long, thin bills are distinctive at long range.

The two stifftails swim low in the water and keep their tails down, except during display. They have noticeably large heads and bills for their size, and short necks.

Dabbling and sieving

This is the preferred technique of the dabbling ducks and is sometimes indulged in by other species, including the swans. There are two main methods of dabbling which can be distinguished, their use being dependent upon the depth of water in which the bird is feeding. In very shallow water, only a few centimetres deep, and too shallow for the birds actually to swim, they will wade slowly along with the tip of the bill just submerged. The head may be hunched back or, together with the neck, stretched forward, and is often swung to and fro as the bird feeds. This method is used to advantage on the lee shore of lakes and reservoirs, where the wind has blown floating seeds and invertebrates into a narrow band.

A variation on this technique can be seen when the birds insert their bills into the mud layer, which, in very shallow water, can contain high concentrations of invertebrates. These conditions can occur at the edges of shallow lakes and pools, as well as in estuaries. Another circumstance is where temporary floods in fields similarly attract dabbling ducks as potential food items get lifted up by the water from the soil or pasture. **Teal**, **Gadwall**, **Mallard** and **Wigeon** all feed in these situations, half on land, half in the water, but the first-named probably does so more regularly than the other three species.

In deeper water, when the birds are swimming, they may have just the tip of their bill submerged but the more usual method is for them to swim with the whole bill and head under water. When using the first technique, they are probably exploiting surface concentrations of food brought together by wind and wave eddies. When swimming with the bill and head under water, they are seeking the abundance of invertebrate life to be found in the top few centimetres of the waterbody. This is especially the case in fertile fresh waters, where a kind of algal soup forms. It is unlikely in these circumstances that they are using their eyes to find individual food particles, as the water tends to be very cloudy and visibility much restricted. Sight may,

A party of Teal dabble in some shallows. The standing birds are holding their body and head low so that their bills are nearly parallel with the surface. Swimming birds may feed like this for surface debris or immerse the whole head to reach suspended or bottom items.

however, be important in locating denser patches. All the dabbling ducks feed in this way, but particularly **Wigeon**, **Gadwall**, **Mallard**, **Teal** and **Shoveler**. **Pintail** and **Garganey** have only occasionally been recorded doing so.

In addition to the dabbling ducks, the **Mandarin** obtains a lot of food by dabbling. Several species among the diving ducks and seaducks also dabble on occasions, if not very often, usually in order to exploit a particular food abundance. For example, **Tufted Duck** will feed in surface shallows on spilt grain, while **Scaup** and **Goldeneye** take items, including grain, floating from sewer outlets in rivers and estuaries. At a few localities this becomes a predominant food source and the birds feed almost exclusively from the surface. **Red-crested Pochard** are perhaps the most regular surface feeders among the diving ducks, in some places spending a majority of their time in this activity.

A number of variations of surface feeding occur. **Teal**, for example, may swim with the bill lying flat along the surface of the water where food is particularly abundant. **Mallard** have been seen paddling vigorously with their feet or up-ending briefly in very shallow water before then indulging in surface dabbling. They were presumably stirring up the mud and bringing any food items closer to the surface. A further effective way of stirring up the mud and water, which seems to be more regularly carried out by the Mallard than by any other species, is actually swimming backwards, combining this with much foot-paddling.

The actual mechanics of feeding on the surface depend on the size of food particle available. Virtually all wildfowl with the exception of a few of the seaducks will peck at individual food items, such as seeds or invertebrates, picking them up singly or in small groups in the tip of the bill. The maximum size they will take is related to the size of their bill. Mallard will frequently take particles up to about a centimetre in diameter, and occasionally much larger. Teal rarely seem to take items more than about 2.5 mm across.

For reasonably dense concentrations of much smaller food particles, however, when it would be very inefficient to attempt to pick them up singly, the dabbling ducks indulge in sieving. This technique involves using the long, narrow tongue, which at rest lies in a groove down the centre of the lower mandible. During this type of feeding, the tongue is moved rapidly up and down. This produces a strong pumping action, which has the effect of sucking in water through the slightly opened tip of the bill and then squirting it out again at the sides. In order to do this, the bird may swim with just the bill tip, or with virtually the whole bill submerged. It does not seem to matter that the expelled water is coming out below the surface. If one watches a duck feeding this way close to, the expelled water can be seen as it emerges from the sides of the bill.

Comb-like serrations, called lamellae, lie along each side of both upper and lower mandibles and act as a filter, catching the food items and allowing the water to pass through. When the bill is held slightly open, the lamellae just overlap to fill the gap. A Mallard typically has about 40–50 lamellae along each side of each mandible, evenly spaced like the teeth of a comb and placed slightly less than a millimetre apart. Every so often the feeding bird cleans the food off the inside of the lamellae with its tongue and swallows it. Such a filter will trap small seeds and tiny invertebrates down to about 1 mm in size. The filter structure of

*A male Teal sieves tiny particles of food from the surface of the water.
Dabbling ducks use their tongue to pump water in through the tip of
their bill and squirt it out through the fine comb-like lamellae along
the sides of each mandible, trapping small seeds and invertebrates.*

the other species is roughly in proportion to the size of their bill,
so that the smaller **Teal** and **Garganey** are capable of trapping
smaller food items than the **Mallard** or **Gadwall**.

While all the dabbling ducks have this filter system, that of
one species has become more highly adapted than in the others.
The very large, spatulate bill which is such a distinctive feature of
the **Shoveler** has a much larger cross-section at the tip and is
therefore capable of sucking up much greater volumes of water
than the smaller bills of other ducks. In addition, the all-
important lamellae are longer and more closely spaced than in
any other species. When they intermesh they form an extremely
fine filter capable of holding much tinier food particles, such as
freshwater plankton. Shovelers feed with just the bill tip
submerged or with the whole head and bill underwater. The two
techniques seem to vary in frequency in different locations,
suggesting that there is an adaptation to local food availability.

Most dabbling ducks feed in flocks, for safety, but Shoveler do so in order to gain an additional benefit. They regularly indulge in communal feeding behaviour, when pairs or small groups swim together in a tight circle while surface-feeding. The head of one bird closely follows the tail of the next, and the combined action of the paddling feet of the swimming birds is presumably extremely effective in stirring up the water and increasing the amount of available food by bringing it closer to the surface. Single Shovelers may sometimes be seen spinning round and round in a very tight circle, the resultant whirlpool helping to produce the same desired effect.

Head underwater and up-ending

Only a proportion of the food available in water, fresh or salt, is going to be on or close to the surface. Most will be at greater depths, whether plants growing on the bottom, molluscs and crustaceans concealed in the bottom silt, or free-swimming animals such as fish. One obvious way of obtaining food from under the water is shown by the swans, which have evolved extra-long necks so that they can reach down with their bills to pluck submerged aquatic vegetation. The body remains horizontal on the surface but the head and neck allows a **Mute Swan**, for example, to feed in water down to about 45 cm in depth, with the **Whooper Swan** not far behind. On average, swans feeding like this keep their heads underwater for about ten seconds. Of the geese, the **Greylag, Canada** and **Brent** all regularly take aquatic vegetation in this way, the other species doing so less commonly.

A swan, goose or duck can greatly extend its underwater reach if, instead of just extending its head and neck underwater, it up-ends into a vertical position, tail in the air, so that the fore part of the body is underwater, too. The wildfowl that do this have the ability to balance when floating vertically in the water, head down and tail up, using the legs and feet as balancing aids. Their buoyancy enables them to float with rather more than half their body length under the water, which, with the extension given by the neck and head, allows species to reach to considerable depths in relation to their size.

The **Mute** and **Whooper Swans** are reckoned to be able to reach down to nearly 1 metre, while the largest goose species, such as **Canada Goose**, can probably make 75 cm. The **Brent Goose**, one of the smallest geese, is a frequent up-ender extending its bill down to about 45–50 cm. The **Pintail** has the longest neck among the ducks and this enables it to reach down the furthest,

Competition for food can be a problem between closely related birds using the same habitat. The varying neck lengths of up-ending wildfowl enable them to feed at different depths and so make the underwater plants and animals go further. From the left are Whooper Swan, Teal, Pintail and Mallard.

to about 50 cm, compared with about 40–45 cm for the **Mallard** whereas the short-necked **Teal** can only manage about 20–25 cm.

This separation between the species is very important, because it increases feeding opportunities within any given water. It is a fact that no two species exploit exactly the same feeding niche, even though there can be considerable overlap, particularly where food is abundant. By being able to reach down to different depths, the various species of swans and ducks can feed in the same piece of water while avoiding direct competition for the same feeding areas. The short-necked birds can occupy the shallowest waters, the longer-necked birds feeding successively further and further out into deeper water.

Eiders, although primarily diving birds taking food items from the bottom of the sea, frequently feed with just their head and neck underwater or up-end in shallows like a dabbling duck. They do this most often in tidal areas such as estuaries, where they feed on mussels. Eiders are not particularly good at walking (*see* below) and so wish to avoid coming on to firm ground in order to feed, for example when the mussel beds are fully exposed at low tide. They prefer instead to feed on the mussels when they are covered by a maximum of about 15 cm of water, and so just comfortably within reach.

Eiders have evolved an extension of this head-underwater or up-ending feeding behaviour which they adopt once they have eaten the more accessible mussels. Sitting fairly upright in the water, they paddle vigorously with their feet, pushing the dead mussel shells aside and exposing new layers. The action is not too

A male Common Eider increases the available food supply by paddling vigorously with its feet in shallow water, stirring up the bottom mud and releasing small molluscs and crustaceans into the water. It will then upend and use its bill to explore the hole it has created. When the tide goes out these shallow, circular depressions remain as evidence of its efforts.

dissimilar to that of a hen scratching at the ground. The ducks then up-end again to explore the hole that has been dug with the feet and then work around it in a circle, probing with the bill. When the tide goes out further, these circles can be seen in the mussel beds, looking just like small craters. The preferred depth for this feeding behaviour seems to be about 15 cm of water, and as the tide ebbs or flows, the ducks move in and out from the shore exploiting the fullest extent of the mussel bed.

Up-ending is a quite energy-intensive method of feeding and the time spent with the head submerged is therefore comparatively short. The **Mute Swan** has been timed up-ending for an average of thirteen seconds, while the **Whooper Swan** can up-end for between ten and twenty seconds. Feeding bouts can be quite intensive and last a long time, with short pauses between groups of up-ending as the bird recovers from the effort. Up-ending ducks keep their heads underwater for a much shorter time, as would be expected, with the **Mallard** usually managing between five and ten seconds.

There is one drawback to up-ending as a feeding method: the up-ending birds are effectively blind to danger, while at the same time a substantial part of the body is visible to a potential predator. For this reason, up-ending is an appropriate feeding behaviour for gregarious species such as wildfowl and only rarely indulged in by a bird on its own.

An up-ending bird can be quite difficult to identify, as a lot of the clues which would normally help the observer are beneath the water. It is usually possible to say whether it is a swan, a goose or a duck, but sometimes not much more than that. Even the tails of wildfowl, however, can be diagnostic if one is denied the opportunity to wait for the whole bird to reappear. The most useful specific difference is that between the **Mute Swan** and the **Whooper** and **Bewick's Swans**: the **Mute Swan**'s tail is elongated and comes to an acute point, whereas the tails of the other two are shorter and very rounded. This difference can actually be detected at greater ranges and in conditions of light which can preclude identification by the more usual bill shape and colour. Unfortunately, it is no use for distinguishing between Whooper and Bewick's; one has to rely on size and proportions of head and neck length, as usual.

The other very striking rear end is that of the **Pintail**, especially the male with its long central tail feathers, but also the female, which has a longer and more pointed rear than any other duck. The tail of the male Pintail is often depressed so that the long feathers lie nearly horizontal to the surface of the water, presumably to help the bird balance.

Wigeon feeding on pieces of vegetation brought to the surface by an up-ending Whooper Swan. The swan is reaching down to as much as a metre below the surface, far out of the reach of the Wigeon. However, as the swan brings the plant leaves and stems to the surface, pieces break off providing the Wigeon with a free meal. Coots often parasitize Whooper and Mute Swans in the same way.

Although up-ending extends the feeding range of short-necked ducks such as **Wigeon**, there is often abundant plant food beyond their maximum depth of 25–30 cm. To overcome their handicap they have found a particularly neat way of getting at such supplies, by relying on other, better-equipped, species to do the hard work for them and bring the food within their reach. When up-ending Mute and Whooper Swans pluck at underwater vegetation they do not do so particularly cleanly, and, as well as the beakfuls which they bring to the surface, other pieces break off and float upwards. In some places it is quite common to see a cluster of Wigeon around each up-ending swan, parasitizing the bigger bird. A similar relationship can be seen with Coots, which dive to bring up vegetation.

I have seen large numbers of both Coots and Mute and Whooper Swans helping to feed equally large numbers of Wigeon on a rich growth of tasselweed in a Scottish loch, as well as on eelgrass in the brackish waters of The Fleet in Dorset. The long string-like leaves of eelgrass are even plucked at by the Wigeon as the food dangles from the swans' beaks.

Gadwall not infrequently obtain some of their food by parasitizing other species, including other ducks, such as the Red-crested Pochard and the Goldeneye, as well as the Coot. On the Bodensee, in Germany, several hundred Gadwall have been seen feeding exclusively on aquatic plants brought to the surface by large flocks of diving Coots.

Surface feeding, whether by dabbling or by sieving, as well as up-ending, is beyond the capabilities of small cygnets or ducklings. While they are very small, they feed mainly by pecking more or less at random at small objects on the surface. They are attracted to contrasting colours and learn by experience what is edible and what is not. **Mallard** ducklings have been observed up-ending from the age of about one week. Broods of ducklings are normally accompanied solely by the mother duck, which acts as a guard, indicating danger as well as brooding the young while they are small enough to fit under her, but not in any way helping them to feed. Cygnets are helped to feed by the parents, which bring submerged plants up to the surface and deposit them in front of their young, thus also showing them what is edible.

DIVING AND FEEDING UNDERWATER

For a bird to dive effectively it has to reduce its buoyancy. Well-adapted diving birds do this by compressing their plumage and squeezing out the not inconsiderable amounts of air trapped in the feathers, and especially in the down layer next to the skin. They are also helped both in getting under the water and in staying there by having their feet set well back on the body. Indeed, the further back the feet, the more accomplished that species is as a diver and the less able it is to walk on land. The way the different wildfowl move around and feed on land will be dealt with later.

The really well-adapted diving ducks, in particular the mergansers, scoters and **Long-tailed Duck**, submerge smoothly and without a splash, putting their head and neck underwater, the body following with little apparent effort. The bulkier **Common Eider** is nearly as adept as these species at diving, as is the **Goldeneye**. The freshwater diving ducks, the **Tufted Duck**

A male Long-tailed Duck slides easily beneath the surface. The seaducks are much more expert divers than the so-called diving ducks and disappear beneath the surface without splashing. Longtails normally dive to a maximum of 10 metres, staying down for anything up to a minute, although dives to 55 metres have been recorded.

and **Pochard,** and also the more marine **Scaup** all give a little forward and upward jump, arching the body and pointing the head and bill downwards as they submerge. The impetus enables them to submerge readily, although often with a bit of a splash. Since the only other freshwater or brackish-water species to behave similarly is the **Coot,** this is a good diagnostic feature at long range for this group of ducks.

When the dabbling ducks dive, they generally do so with much thrashing of the wings, the whole act of submerging looking, as it undoubtedly is, something of an effort. A **Pintail,** when diving, brings its head back over its shoulders and then plunges forwards with slightly opened wings and causing a considerable splash. This ungainliness is even more apparent on the relatively rare occasions when geese or swans dive.

The manner in which a bird submerges is related, in most cases, to the way in which it propels itself while underwater. Thus, the dabbling ducks not only use their wings to help force themselves down beneath the surface, they continue to use them while actually underwater, as it were flying through the water. Nearly all the diving ducks, freshwater and marine, rely mainly

A Red-breasted Merganser 'flying' through the water. Only this species regularly uses its wings underwater and then not always. The wings are not opened until the bird is submerged thus avoiding heavy splashing which might alert fish which the Merganser is seeking to catch.

on their feet and hence do not need to open the wings as they dive. The exceptions are the Common Eider, the Common Scoter and the Red-breasted Merganser.

The **Common Eider** and the **Common Scoter** half open their wings just before slipping under the surface, although once there they use only their feet. It is possible that a single shove with the wings helps the bird on its way. This view is reinforced by the observations that the Common Scoter makes more use of its wings in diving in rough water than it does when conditions are calm. It is clearly then harder to submerge.

The **Red-breasted Merganser**, unlike its close relative the Goosander, does use its wings underwater, although there is some disagreement among observers as to the regularity with which this happens, some indicating that it is the norm and others that it happens only occasionally. What is agreed, though, is that the wings are not opened until the bird is submerged, thus avoiding any splashing.

Close observations of birds underwater are difficult to make, although opportunities do sometimes occur, for example, when looking down into clear water from a cliff top. Individual birds have also been studied in glass-sided tanks. The feet are used both for propulsion and for steering, although some species also use the tail for steering. The Common Scoter's tail has been noted as being distinctly fanned as it dives. The mergansers certainly use their tails underwater, while the stifftails, the **Ruddy Duck** and **White-headed Duck**, are named for their distinctive tail, which is comprised of long and comparatively rigid feathers. Making up one-fifth of body length it forms an important rudder for the birds while swimming underwater.

Seeking their prey

The majority of wildfowl which feed underwater do so by diving in a likely area and then seeking out their food either visually in clear water or by touch in murkier conditions. These birds are taking either plant material, the leaves and stems of aquatic

The Long-tailed Duck (upper), Smew (middle) and Pochard (lower) all dive to obtain their food but the shape and structure of the bill of each of them reveals their different diets. The small but stout bill of the Longtail is used to grasp and crush molluscs and crustaceans. The Smew has a long, thin bill with sharp serrations along the edges which help it to grasp slippery fish. The Pochard feeds mainly on underwater plants which it plucks at with its long and broad bill.

vegetation, or invertebrates such as molluscs and crustaceans, which are either stationary or comparatively slow-moving. Thus, once having located a promising area or a particular food source, such as an area of dense underwater plants or perhaps a mussel bed, the bird merely has to dive again and again in the same vicinity. Different species, such as the **Pochard**, which is primarily a vegetarian, and the **Tufted Duck**, which takes mainly animal food, are able to feed in the same area because of their differences in diet.

The same is true for species which penetrate to different depths. Thus, Scaup, scoters, Long-tailed Ducks, Goldeneyes and eiders may all occur in the same area of sea and all be feeding from the bottom on molluscs and crustaceans, but, because there are shallow-diving species such as Scaup and eiders and deep divers like Long-tailed Duck and scoter, competition between them is avoided.

The two common sawbill ducks, the **Goosander** and the **Red-breasted Merganser**, feed predominantly on fish, including fast-moving species such as salmon and trout. Where they can locate a shoal of fish, they will submerge and then give chase, but more usually they adopt a more energy-saving technique for locating fish before diving. This they do by swimming with just their head and neck underwater, looking for suitable prey, and then on sighting it they submerge quickly and smoothly. So, a Goosander or a Red-breasted Merganser seen swimming with its head and neck submerged is not actually feeding, as would be a Common Eider or a Mallard behaving similarly, but on the lookout for food; the aquatic equivalent of a hovering kestrel.

Several species of seaduck indulge in mass feeding, with some instances of cooperative feeding, where the presence of several birds together aids them all in obtaining food. A flock of **Common Scoter** will show considerable synchrony of diving, with virtually all the birds underwater together.

The exponents of co-operative feeding are the **Red-breasted Merganser** and the **Goosander**. They frequently hunt in pairs, the two birds pursuing the same fish, but the most obvious example of cooperation is when a whole flock forms a line of diving birds, which effectively pushes shoals of fish into shallower water where they are easier to catch. This is very distinctive behaviour and exciting to watch.

The **Ruddy Duck** and the **White-headed Duck** feed in a different way from all other diving ducks, swimming along near the bed of a lake and sifting food items from the bottom ooze. They swing their heads from side to side as they move, their bills opening and closing in a pumping action.

Staying down

While the manner in which a duck dives can be indicative of a species or group, so, too, can the time spent underwater and the distance between the place of diving and that of reappearing, which tend to be related. The freshwater diving ducks, **Pochard** and **Tufted Duck**, rarely stay down for more than 30 seconds and more usually for only fifteen to twenty seconds. This latter range is sufficient to take them to depths of from 1–2 m, while the longer period allows them to reach down to as much as 4 metres with a probable maximum of 5–6 m. In both species, the males' dives are on average deeper and longer than those of the females, allowing a greater exploitation of the available food resource. On the whole, the shorter dives do not allow for much sideways movement and the birds tend to surface quite close to where they submerged.

The dives of dabbling ducks are generally much shorter than for the diving ducks, with five seconds recorded for **Shoveler** and up to ten seconds for the **Mallard**, which has been recorded as descending to depths of about 80 cm.

Diving habits, as well as being used to help identify the species of wildfowl, can inform the observer of some of the characteristics of the waterbody concerned. In eutrophic fresh waters, the bulk of lowland waters in England, the high density of plankton and silt in the water prevents the light from penetrating very far, so limiting the depth at which either plants or invertebrates can flourish. The presence of flocks of **Pochard** will indicate a good growth of underwater plants. Furthermore, the often erratic nature of Pochard use of different waters, with large numbers present in some winters and virtually none in others, can be explained in terms of cycles of abundance of underwater plants over a period of years in response to changes in concentrations of nutrients, particularly nitrates.

Freshwater diving ducks like the **Pochard** and **Tufted Duck** can select the area of the lake or reservoir which contains the food they want at the depths they are comfortable with. Their marine cousin, the **Scaup**, has the complicating factor of the tide to cope with. It dives to a similar maximum depth, of 5 or 6 m, although the majority of dives are to no more than 3 to 4 m, and its underwater time, averaging between 15–30 seconds, is also much the same.

Because the depth of water varies during the tidal cycle, Scaup either have to vary their feeding area as a consequence or, if the molluscs on which they mainly feed in winter have a restricted distribution, then they have to confine their feeding to those periods at which the depth of water is within their diving capability. In most localities, this means that around high tide flocks of Scaup will show very little activity, the majority of the birds sleeping with their heads tucked under their wings.

The **Common Eider** is a another species whose feeding is controlled by the tide. Its maximum diving depth has been recorded as 15–20 m, but this is an extreme depth and the vast

A diving male Tufted Duck holds its wings tightly closed and uses its feet for propulsion. Dives are usually to about three to five metres, staying down for no more than half a minute. Just before submerging, diving ducks compress their plumage to squeeze out as much as possible of the air trapped in the down and feathers.

majority of feeding dives are to no more than 5 m. Eiders normally spend no more than 40 seconds underwater, but times of up to 78 seconds have been recorded. In shallow water, Eiders can move many metres underwater, presumably probing along the bottom seeking crustaceans and molluscs. They also take small fish, such as sticklebacks and gobies, which live among rocks and seaweed, and it may be that pursuit of these prolongs their dives and increase the distance travelled.

One of the deepest divers among the wildfowl is the **Long-tailed Duck**. There are authenticated records of birds getting entangled in fishing nets set to depths of as much as 55 m. Such depths are exceptional, though, as large numbers of Long-tailed Ducks winter in much shallower water and clearly find all the food they want. Dives to 3–10 m seem to be the most common with submergence times of 30–60 seconds. This length of time allows the diving bird to move considerable distances underwater, and it can be quite frustrating watching for one to surface, particularly at long range and in anything but calm water or if there are waves to make observation harder.

Common and **Velvet Scoters** feed mainly on molluscs living on the sea bottom and seek them in greatly varying depths. Although many flocks winter in comparatively shallow water and feed in about 2–5 m, others stay out in much deeper water and regularly dive to 10–20 m with a maximum of 30 m. Diving times in shallow water average 20–30 seconds, but this will be extended to as much as 60–65 seconds in greater depths, although the distance travelled remains small.

The **Goldeneye** is another diving species taking mainly molluscs and crustaceans from the bottom. As well as breeding beside fresh water, quite large numbers winter on fresh water as well as on the sea. Most diving is in water of no more than 4 m in depth, with diving times of between fifteen and twenty seconds. As with the freshwater diving ducks, which in some ways this species more closely resembles than it does the seaducks, the males are more proficient divers than the females, going deeper and staying down longer.

The fish-eating sawbills are feeding on mobile prey and can cover quite long distances while submerged. Some dives are carried out almost vertically, while others are on a long slant. All three species, **Smew**, **Red-breasted Merganser** and **Goosander**, feed mainly in quite shallow water, rarely over 6 m in depth, but the Goosander is also found in much deeper water, down to 35 m or more. In those depths, it may stay down for nearly a minute, but most dives, as for the other two species, are usually in the range 20–40 seconds.

The stifftails feed in quite shallow water, rarely more than 3–4 m, but stay down for comparatively long, 20–40 seconds, during which they can cover several metres horizontally.

The ducklings of the diving species of duck can all dive when only a day or two old, although many of them in fact peck at surface items in the same way as the ducklings of dabbling ducks, at least for the first few days. The young of species such as the **Long-tailed Duck** can, in captivity, dive and catch water shrimps with considerable skill when only a few days old. The young **Ruddy Duck** can dive remarkably efficiently from the day it hatches, staying down for several seconds right from the start.

Obtaining and dealing with prey

The bills of the different diving ducks are as well adapted for the purpose of obtaining and dealing with their prey as are those of the dabbling ducks. With the exception of the very specialized sawbills, they are all much stouter and deeper in cross-section. Those of the **Tufted Duck** and **Pochard** are used for picking up small invertebrates and plucking vegetation and are comparatively small and narrow for the size of the bird.

Among the seaducks, the eiders, scoters, **Goldeneye** and **Longtail**, all feed on molluscs and crustaceans and need to be able both to pick them up and then to crush their shells. Their bills are quite deep, and the comparatively large heads of these species help to house the necessary muscles. The stoutest bill is the large wedge of the **Common Eider**, which is used both for digging in the substrate and for crushing shells.

The generic term 'sawbill', applied to the mergansers and Goosander, describes their elongated bills, which have sharp serrations along the sides of both mandibles. These are the equivalent of the fine filters of the dabbling ducks, but in this case enlarged and hardened to act as teeth and help grip the slippery fish on which they feed. The 'nail' at the tip of the upper mandible is shaped into a distinct hook overhanging the lower mandible, as a further aid to grasping.

All the diving species swallow the majority of their food underwater. Only the largest items are brought to the surface to be dealt with. For example, **Common Eiders** can frequently be seen manipulating crabs which they have caught but cannot deal with easily. There is undoubtedly a practical value in swallowing the food before surfacing, as this makes it harder for parasitic birds, such as gulls, to obtain food from the ducks as they emerge. It is quite common to see Herring and Great Black-backed Gulls sitting on the sea close to diving ducks, such as eiders and scoters, flapping up and hovering over the surfacing bird and trying to snatch the food from it. The synchronous diving mentioned above may well be a further defence against this parasitism by making it harder for the gulls to select a victim as virtually the whole flock surfaces at once.

MOVING AND FEEDING ON LAND

Not for nothing is the word 'waddle' used as the popular description of a duck walking on land. Although all the wildfowl can and do walk, most of them are rather ungainly and some, notably the diving and sea ducks find it awkward and walk only for very short distances, usually when nesting. This is because their legs are set well back on their bodies. This makes for very efficient diving and swimming underwater, but there is a penalty to pay in being rather clumsy on land.

All the swans walk quite adequately, although 'waddling' could certainly apply to the **Mute Swan**, which sways from side to side as it walks. So, too, if not quite so obviously, do **Whooper** and **Bewick's Swans**. The latter, indeed, is quite neat on its feet and walks with some ease. It is a fairly common, but mistaken belief that the Mute Swan is unable to land on firm ground and that therefore it must always walk from adjoining water. However, it frequently feeds in fields some distance from the nearest water and can land on them relatively easily, although landing is obviously not so graceful as when performed by a lighter bird.

The geese are easily the most terrestrial of all the waterfowl, being fully adapted to feeding on land, which all species do to a greater or lesser extent. All will feed in water, as already described, but only in a few localities is this the predominant method, for example where there are underwater eelgrass beds which **Brent Geese** can reach by up-ending, or where **Greylags** feed in freshwater marshes.

Walking geese hold their neck nearly vertical and their head horizontal, the body evenly poised on the legs, which are at about the mid position. There is little or no side-to-side waddling, theirs is a well-balanced mode of progressing. If necessary, geese can break easily into a run, when the head and neck tend to be stretched a little further forward. Running is rarely necessary when flying is quicker, but during the summer moult, when the birds have lost their main flight feathers, then running becomes an important safety factor.

A flock of flightless geese can easily outrun a man (this may seem an odd concept, but it does in fact happen, although one

hopes it will not when trying to round up flightless geese in order to ring them). They can also use their speed to get to water and safety from ground predators such as foxes or wolves.

Typically, flocks of geese graze on short vegetation, or probe in soft substrates for roots and underground tubers. Grazing geese seize an individual blade of grass or growing corn in their bills, then jerk their heads back to sever it from the plant. The neck of a grazing goose is held horizontal, with the head bent down close to the ground, so the total movement during feeding is kept to a minimum, which allows a very fast feeding rate.

When grazing on a fairly even sward, **Barnacle Geese** can average about 200 pecks per minute. Not only do they regularly feed at such a tremendous rate, but while doing so they are not feeding at random, grasping any bit of grass which presents itself, but the feeding birds are selecting only the green leaves, which are the most nutritious, and are avoiding the tougher stems and brown, dead leaves. The force needed to break off a green blade of grass is rather less than for a tough, old one, and it seems likely that the geese, even if they grasp one of the latter in error, can realize that it is unsuitable as food when it fails to break after the bird has given its usual jerk upwards with the head.

Other distinctive feeding methods adopted by geese on land include stripping seeds from sedge (**Barnacle Geese**), plucking long strands of eelgrass (**Brent Geese**), and probing soft mud and moss. This last method is commonly used by larger-billed species, especially the **Greylag** and the Greenland race of **White-fronted Geese**. With their long, wedge-shaped bills they probe through the surface mat of vegetation and, by feel, locate the roots, tubers and stolons of marsh and bog plants. These are rich in easily digestible starch. The head of a goose which is feeding in this way can be seen pushing forwards and downwards as it probes and then being sharply jerked backwards as it grasps the food item and seeks to break it off the retaining roots. The feeding birds leave behind them telltale holes in the surface of the marsh or bog which are unmistakable signs that these species of geese have fed there.

All wildfowl can walk but their different builds mean that for some, like the Bean Goose (bottom), with its body well balanced over its legs, walking is easy and they can also run smoothly and fast. The much heavier Whooper Swan (middle) can walk, though with a somewhat waddling gait, while running is not really possible. The Common Scoter (top) rarely goes on land; the position of its legs and feet, set well back on the body for efficient swimming underwater, make walking much more of an exertion.

The **Egyptian Goose** and shelducks are equally at home on land as the true geese. The former is a grazing species, feeding on grass and farmland like the geese. Shelducks generally feed below the high-tide line, obtaining small invertebrates and molluscs from close to the surface of mud and sand by digging, dabbling and scything, as well as occasionally up-ending. Among the wildfowl only shelducks scythe. A bird feeding in this way inserts the tip of its bill into the first centimetre or so of the soft surface and then walks slowly forwards, swinging its head to and fro. In this way, it can sift through more mud or soft sand for each pace forwards. A scything bird leaves behind it a very distinctive zigzag pattern overlaid with its footprints.

The dabbling ducks can all walk quite well, and most can even run when it is essential, their bodies held fairly horizontal. The **Wigeon** is the only species which regularly feeds on land, grazing like geese in dense flocks on short grass. Other species feed on land if there is an attractive source of food there, if only bread scattered for **Mallards** in a town park.

A **Tufted Duck** or a **Pochard** on land does not look very comfortable, an eider even less so. All of these diving ducks and seaducks have to adopt a quite upright stance to maintain their balance. A few of them do feed on land occasionally, perhaps the most regular being the Tufted Duck, which in town parks can be almost as active on land as a Mallard in seeking food offered by members of the public, although when a Tufted Duck tries to hurry towards some titbit it borders on a comical spectacle.

Although awkward in stance and comparatively slow in walking, all the other species of seaduck can walk adequately. Indeed, several species may nest many hundreds of metres from the nearest water and be forced to walk such distances when escorting their young to the water. The **Goldeneye** probably nests the furthest from water on a regular basis, with up to 1 km or even more not unusual. The female may fly to and fro during incubation, but once the young have hatched she is faced with walking, with them, the full distance to the selected water, which may not always be the nearest. Presumably the selection is made by the female on the basis of food supply for herself and the ducklings rather than proximity to the nest.

The two introduced species, the **Mandarin** and the **Wood Duck**, are put into the group of perching ducks for the very good reason that they are quite at home among trees growing close to or actually in the water. They perch very readily on overhanging branches and any fallen trunks or timber protruding from the water. They can both land and take off from such perches. They also walk quickly and easily on dry land.

Four Dark-bellied Brent Geese and a pair of Shelduck feeding in an estuary. The Brent Geese, which feed mainly on land, are grazing on eel-grass Zostera, *a long, stringy marine grass, while the Shelducks, equally at home on the land or in the water, are walking through the shallows sifting small invertebrates from the layer of very soft mud just covered by the water.*

FLYING

Evolution having resulted in birds being able to fly, the birds themselves make use of this ability for a number of different purposes. Among wildfowl, the most important ways in which flight is exploited are for migration and for moving between feeding and roosting places. Only a few species include flight as an element in their display, unlike so many other kinds of birds.

A migratory flight involves preparation. The initial stimulus for spring migration among birds wintering in European latitudes comes from the increase in daylength past an initial threshold. Physiological changes encourage the deposition of fat, particularly beneath the skin (subcutaneous) and inside the abdomen (visceral). Fat is the vital fuel used by migrating birds, which often have to cross long stretches of sea or perhaps desert where feeding opportunities are either non-existent or very limited.

Wildfowl preparing for migration therefore increase their food intake in order to lay down that vital fat, and this shows itself in increased time spent feeding. Conveniently, for plant-eating species such as the grazing geese and Wigeon, the onset of spring growth in the plants means higher levels of nutrients in the growing tips on which the birds feed.

Having gained weight and got into condition for migration, birds normally wait for suitable weather conditions before setting out. It makes sense to avoid head winds which would prolong the journey, although studies have shown that migration will commence as often with side winds as with the obviously favourable tail winds. The birds cannot afford to wait indefinitely and so will set out in less than optimal conditions if they have to. Similarly, clear skies are preferred to overcast, but are not essential.

Although the number of wildfowl migrating into, out of and across Europe can be numbered in millions, the actual act of migration is surprisingly difficult to observe. Much of it takes place at night and at high altitude. Only at a few favoured places, such as headlands jutting out into the sea, is it sometimes possible to see wildfowl actually on the move. One such place is Dungeness in Kent, where in some autumns thousands of **Common Scoters** have been seen passing close inshore. There is a regular migration of these ducks through the English Channel, but it takes comparatively rare weather conditions to bring them down close to the sea and then close to land.

The most one can expect to see at all regularly is birds arriving after having completed a migration or, less often, departing on migration. **Barnacle Geese** arriving on the island of Islay, Inner Hebrides, having flown from Iceland, a distance of about 1100 km, generally do so on a northerly wind which will have quite possibly halved their journey. The normal ground speed of Barnacle Geese is about 50 kph, equivalent to a strong to gale-force wind.

The geese are usually in small flocks of between ten and 200 birds, and typically an arrival lasts for many hours, or even a day or two. It is not known in what sized flocks they depart from Iceland, but it is unlikely to be a mass departure, more probably taking place over a period of as many hours as the arrival. The Barnacle Geese have probably flown most of the way at considerable heights, in common with most migration as this enables the birds to avoid obstructions and turbulence, which is prevalent close to the ground or sea. Although the geese could, if they wanted, land on the sea, unlike most other migratory birds, there seems little reason for them to do so when they could be exposed to severe wave action. There is certainly no feeding available to them there.

When the geese actually arrive on Islay, they have lost most of this height by the time they are visible, sometimes hugging the waves, or at most a hundred metres or so up. Once they have made a landfall, the birds touch down on the exposed sandflats at the head of a northerly-facing sealoch and immediately start bathing and preening, all the while keeping up a constant calling, presumably re-establishing family links.

Having achieved the first priority of tidying up their plumage, the next requirement is for sleep. This takes precedence over feeding, even though there are lush pastures within a few hundred metres over the sea wall. During a day of arrivals, the sandflats gradually fill up with sleeping geese, others landing among them, bathing and preening and then in their turn tucking their heads under their wings and sleeping. Only after several hours do the first birds awaken and make the short flight to begin grazing on the nearby fields.

Such arrivals can be seen in autumn at other major goose haunts and at some places where **Whooper** and **Bewick's Swans** spend the winter, but there is generally much less to see during departure in spring. Not only do the majority of birds seem to depart after dark, presumably so as not to reduce daylight feeding time, but wildfowl seem to make rather little fuss about their leaving on migration. Some observers have reported increased noise and flying around in the days or even hours beforehand, but there is little hard evidence to suggest that this is, in fact, what has been described for captive passerines as migratory restlessness. Just occasionally, the observer may become aware that the flock of geese he or she has been watching has taken off and is heading steadily away northwards, climbing determinedly and obviously not going to turn back or land locally, but with no other sign that this is a migration flight.

NON-MIGRATORY FLIGHTS

Although true migration over long distances is of seasonal occurrence, all wildfowl fly every day, the major reason being to move between their roosting place and their chosen feeding site. In shooting areas, many dabbling ducks and some diving ducks have adapted to feed at night and roost during the day. Often enough they use the same roosting sites as geese, which, however, follow the reverse pattern. Thus one can observe geese, such as the **Pinkfoot** and **Greylag**, flighting out from a roosting water at dawn as **Mallard** and **Teal** flight in, both feeding on surrounding farmland.

Another reason for flight is to avoid predators, and the smaller wildfowl are both fast and agile. Teal, in particular, will fly in dense flocks and are capable of tight synchronized turns that would not disgrace a flock of waders or Starlings. The smaller species of geese, too, **Brent** and **Barnacle Geese**, will also sometimes indulge in mass manoeuvres of this kind.

A full account of the displays of wildfowl will follow in a later chapter. Here it is worth mentioning that some species of duck, especially the dabbling species, use flight in their displays, most obviously when indulging in 'three-bird chases'. This involves two, or more, males pursuing a single female.

TAKING OFF

When wildfowl are thinking of moving, they signal to each other with what are known as 'pre-flight intention movements'. These are designed to attract the attention of others in their vicinity. The most visible part of the bird is its head and neck and it is these that are mainly used in the signalling. The swans and geese shake their head from side to side (head-flagging), while the ducks mainly bob it up and down.

It is often a single bird which starts to signal and, if one watches such a bird and its neighbours carefully, it is possible to

A family party of Bewick's Swans prepares for take-off. The birds are pumping their heads up and down, and quite often shake them from side to side as well, as a signal to each other of their imminent departure. The family unit is very important to swans and geese and the signals help to ensure unanimity of action helping the family members stay together.

see the signalling beginning to spread and increase in intensity until the birds decide to take off. Alternatively, the signalling bird may fail to generate any interest in flight and after a short while will cease to signal and will instead carry on feeding or sleeping. Some species, as well as head-bobbing or head-flagging, open and flap the wings once or twice, another very visible action.

Taking off from the water or ground is comparatively easy for the dabbling ducks, which can spring almost vertically into the air. It is accompanied by quite a splash as they push downwards with their feet and simultaneously flap their wings strongly so that the tips often hit the water. The geese, too, can spring into the air both from the water and from land. The swans and also the diving diving and seaducks require more effort for take-off,

A group of Garganey bob their heads up and down prior to take-off. As with the head-shaking of the swans, the bobbing is a signal to other birds. Although the family unit is not strong in ducks, the pair need to act together as do members of a flock.

involving at least some steps forwards to gain the necessary momentum. This is at its most pronounced in the swans, which have to take several steps while flapping hard, gradually lifting off. If from water, their feet slap on the surface for several paces, a highly audible sound (*see* aggressive displays on page 81). Swans normally take off into the wind to gain more lift.

FORMATION FLYING

One of the most distinctive and well-known features of wildfowl in flight is the V-formation adopted by geese. Swans often fly in this way, too, while among other groups of birds it is probably commonest in the cranes and the gulls. It is the geese, though, that use it most consistently and which have attracted the most attention, and not just among ornithologists. The questions most commonly asked are why they do it and what benefits it brings them. These may seem unnecessary questions, but few, if any, actions of wild animals are without a purpose and many have evolved to bring about definite advantages, to the species and to the individual.

There seem to be three main theories for V-formation flying: first, that it is the easiest way for the birds to maintain visual contact in flight; second, that it is aerodynamically the most efficient, actually reducing the power needed by the birds to fly; and, third, that it performs a signalling function, attracting lost birds to flocks of their own kind. The proponents of these theories have been known to suggest that their explanation is the only one which is true, but there seems no reason why only one should apply and it is equally possible that all three may be true, at least in part. There is certainly no logical reason for them to be thought of as mutually exclusive.

A skein of geese in V-formation showing very even spacing between the birds, a situation only rather rarely encountered in real life, but giving greater theoretical benefit.

The simplest theory, and certainly the most widely held until comparatively recently, is that flying in V-formation is just the obvious way to fly if you want to keep in contact with your fellow geese. As already mentioned when considering pre-flight intention movements, it is very important that individual geese do not get lost. When in flight, therefore, each bird needs to be able to see others in order to stay with them. There are good reasons for not flying immediately behind another bird, because the latter leaves considerable turbulence in its wake. The most visible part of a goose in flight is not its head and body but its tail, which has a bold white stripe at the base, a feature common to all species. This will be conspicuous in poor light and even at night. So, the best place to fly in order to keep sight of a neighbour is behind and to one side. This also fits well with the anatomy of a goose, which has its eyes placed on the sides of its head so that its vision directly forwards is not quite so good as it is out to the side. If one extends the pattern of a goose flying slightly behind and to one side on both sides of a leading bird, one ends up with a formation shaped like a V. We shall return later to the question of who leads.

A considerable amount of work has been done on the possible aerodynamic advantage to flying in a V, including by aerodynamicists, not just by ornithologists. When feeding up prior to migration, large birds such as geese and swans cannot store so much fat in their bodies as smaller birds, because they would become too heavy. A small warbler can double its body weight and still fly. A swan cannot put on more than about 10–15 per cent of its weight. Thus, even a small gain in flight efficiency, leading to a reduction in the energy needed to cover a long distance, would be useful.

It can be shown theoretically that the greatest aerodynamic benefits come if the birds can keep a constant distance apart, at a constant angle to each other, and also beat their wings in complete synchrony. The downbeat of the wing produces a corresponding swirl of rising air behind it which, if the next bird can beat into it at precisely the right point, will give it additional lift, thus reducing the effort needed to maintain height and forward speed. Just watching a skein of flying geese immediately reveals that none of these three conditions is met, or is so only very occasionally. The spacing between the birds changes all the

A flock of Pink-footed Geese migrate under the moon. In common with all geese, their white rumps are very visible to the following bird, helping the flock to stay together on migration and assisting each bird in keeping station with its neighbour.

time, while the wingbeats are rarely together. Furthermore, the birds rarely stay in a level plane but rise and fall relative to each other. However, that is the optimum situation, which has been calculated in one purely theoretical study to lead to a gain in flight efficiency of as much as 70 per cent. Anything less than that, even down to a very small percentage gain, would still help the birds fly further while using less energy.

A different study analysed cine film of flying geese and found that not only was a true V-formation only one way in which geese flew (they also flew in J-shapes and in diagonal lines, as well as in no particular pattern), but there was great variation in the angle of the V, as well as in individual spacing and wingbeat. The conclusion was that on this evidence there was no discernible aerodynamic benefit to the geese.

One of the more difficult concepts to grasp which has been put forward by the theoretical studies is that the leading bird, too, can benefit from its position in the V, although not to so great an extent as the birds behind it.

The third reason put forward for formation flying is that it acts as a signal to other geese, perhaps lost or needing to find more of their kind for safety, that here is the flock that they seek. The suggestion has been made that the way in which the flying birds move and the formations they adopt are different for each species, thus providing more helpful information for the lost or straying birds. It is certainly true that experts can sometimes identify different species of geese at long range in this way, but the theory has never been put to a proper test as it has been, for example, to demonstrate that the smoke-like manoeuvrings of Starlings as they prepare to go to roost is a signal showing other Starlings where the roost is located.

If the V-formation of geese is well known and arouses comment in people otherwise little interested in birds, so too does the question of whether or not there is a lead goose at the head of the V. Wildfowlers have frequently written on this aspect, claiming that it is always an old gander who takes on this role. This is quite likely, but only up to a point. It is certainly not an invariable rule. A flock of geese is composed of family parties and pairs, as well as some younger, unpaired birds. Adult birds are more likely to lead the young than the other way around, although there is little evidence for the male doing more leading than the female either within a family or within a pair. So, it is probable that a flock would be led by an adult, if not invariably a male. However, it is easily observed that the lead in a flying flock changes frequently, different birds forging ahead or coming to the front when there is a slight change of direction. A flock of flying geese has a corporate purpose and direction shared among its component individuals, not directed by a single leader.

If there is an aerodynamic benefit from flying in formation, then one would expect the lead to change fairly regularly so that the lead bird could take a share in the benefit. Indeed, if the lead bird tires more quickly than its followers, then it will be overtaken and another bird will take its place.

While none of the above theories can easily be proven, and given the already stated possibility that all three may have some elements of truth in them, there is a case to be made for Occam's Razor being applied to this subject: select the simplest theory in preference to the more complicated.

Staying in contact

The importance to individuals of staying within a flock was mentioned above (*see* page 46) and will be developed further in the next chapter. Virtually all of the wildfowl have characters which enhance their visibility to others of their kind. The white tail-band of the geese has been discussed in the context of flying in Vs (*see* page 45). Even more obvious is the all-white colouring of swans. The shelducks and **Egyptian Geese** have broad white patches on their forewings which will be especially obvious to a following bird. The vast majority of ducks have white somewhere in their wings and/or tail which will make them more conspicuous in flight particularly to following birds.

Apart from the male **Wigeon**, which has a white forewing, the dabbling ducks' principal visual signal is their speculum, an area of the inner hindwing that is usually coloured green or blue, although it is white in the **Gadwall**. The speculum has a display function between birds of a pair, but when the wings are beating up and down it will also act as a useful aid to conspicuousness, enhanced in most species by a border of one or two narrow white bands. All the diving ducks have white or whitish stripes along the centre of their wings, while, of the seaducks, only the Long-tailed Duck and the Common Scoter do not have at least some patches of white in their wings.

As well as these visual ways of staying in contact, many wildfowl species also use their voices or, in some cases, the noise made by their wings in flight. The geese and **Whooper** and **Bewick's Swans** are the most vocal, each having distinctive calls, and a knowledge of these can be very helpful when trying to identify birds at a distance or in poor light. The sounds are very far-carrying and it is at least possible that, in the same way as has been put forward for the signal function of formation flying, the

calls not only serve to maintain the cohesion of a flock but may also be heard by straying birds, which will be able to join the larger group with all the benefits that brings.

Among the ducks, the species which call most consistently in flight and which can be readily identified from their voices, even in the dark, are the **Wigeon**, with its high-pitched whistling, and the **Teal**, which makes high piping notes. Most other dabbling ducks quack at intervals in flight, but not with the same constancy as the calling of the Wigeon and the Teal.

Most of the diving ducks and seaducks are relatively silent in flight. The one notable exception is the **Long-tailed Duck**, which is extremely vocal. Its yodelling calls, although closely associated

Four Mallard and two Pochard in flight. The patterned wings of all dabbling ducks, also the white tails of these Mallard, and the white wingbars or patches on diving and most seaducks act as a visual signal to following birds in the same way as does the white rump of geese (see page 44).

with display, are also repeated in flight, including at night, and are therefore almost certainly being used as contact calls, too.

The best-known wing noise among all species of birds, and one familiar to anyone living close to a lowland river or lake, is the musical throbbing sound produced by a **Mute Swan** in flight. It is audible at distances of up to 2 km and must certainly help to

The powerful flight of the Mute Swan. Its stiff, curved wing feathers make a distinctive and far-carrying throbbing sound as it flies. The neck is held stretched forward. Close to, the power of the wings can be appreciated as the body can be seen to be lifted up with each down stroke.

keep flying birds in touch with each other, particularly at night. The calls of the Mute Swan, while not non-existent as the name may imply, are much less far-carrying than those of the **Whooper** and **Bewick's,** and the wing noise is a very adequate substitute. The sound is caused by the beating of the stiff and curved flight feathers through the air and not, as has been argued from time to time, by the action of the wing muscles on the chest cavity producing audible exhalations from the lungs. The wings of the Whooper and Bewick's produce an audible swishing sound, but no throbbing comes from their much straighter flight feathers; with their far-carrying trumpeting calls, however, they have little need for any further contact sound.

Several of the ducks produce whistling noises with the wings in flight. One of the noisiest is the **Shoveler,** which makes a

A male Tufted Duck flies fast and low over the water. The whitish wingbar is clearly visible from above and behind and the wings also make a pronounced whistling noise. Both of these function as aids to help keep a flock together. The Tufted Duck is a comparatively silent bird and has evolved these visual and audio signals instead of flight calls.

characteristic drum-like rattling sound as it takes off from the water and then a loud, relatively low-pitched whistling as it flies. The other dabbling ducks, **Mallard** and **Pintail**, are quieter in flight, but the wingbeat whistles of **Tufted Duck** and **Pochard** can be heard at considerable distances. Opportunities for hearing the seaducks in flight are generally limited, but the **Goldeneye's** high-pitched singing sound can be very noticeable.

It seems probable that these wing sounds help the birds to stay together, particularly when flying at night. Most of the diving ducks and seaducks are comparatively silent, having few calls, or calling only during display, and the wingbeat sounds, produced continuously and without additional effort, are a more than adequate substitute for contact calls.

FLIGHTLESSNESS

The feather is a most remarkable structure, combining flexibility with great strength. Many different shapes and forms of feather fulfil a wide variety of purposes. Groups of long, stiff feathers combine to produce an aerodynamic shape which can support the weight of the bird, while softer, downy-edged feathers provide a dense body-clothing layer which is both insulating and waterproof. There is just one drawback. Feathers have a comparatively short lifetime. They wear out, gradually becoming frayed and worn so losing their vital properties.

As a general rule, every feather on a bird's body is replaced at least once a year. Sometimes this replacement, particularly of

The white rump of this moulting Canada Goose is much more conspicuous than usual as the main wing feathers have been moulted. The closed wings, when the feathers are fully grown, reach to the tip of the tail. Moulting geese rarely stray far from water during the moult as although they can run quite fast they are much more vulnerable to predators while they lack the powers of flight.

body feathers, is more frequent, happening up to four times a year, and may be linked with changes in plumage colour connected with display and finding a mate, or with the need for camouflage. The full annual moult normally occurs immediately after the end of the breeding season, during which the rate of wear is probably at its greatest, whether the bird is nesting in dense undergrowth, in a hedge or on a cliff ledge. It is also a time of year when food is still relatively abundant, and changing feathers consumes considerable quantities of energy, and provides a new set of feathers prior to any autumn migration and the more taxing times of the winter to come.

With a handful of exceptions, the main wing feathers, the primaries and secondaries which do all the work of providing lift as the bird beats its wings, are changed each year after the breeding season. These are obviously the most tricky feathers to moult and regrow without impairing the bird's ability to fly. Throughout the bird kingdom, nearly all species solve this problem by moulting the feathers very slowly, a few at a time and allowing each replacement to grow nearly to full size before moulting some more. This means that the bird never loses the power of flight, but the moult process necessarily lasts many weeks or even months during which time the bird certainly does not have its full flying ability, even though the impairment may be only slight. The shortest period taken to complete the wing moult among small birds in Europe is about five weeks, and many take as long as eight or ten weeks.

The wildfowl, and a few other groups of birds (principally the divers, grebes and some of the rails), have evolved a different solution to the problem of wing moult. They shed their main flight feathers simultaneously and the new feathers all grow together. This means that until the new feathers have grown the birds are incapable of flight, although, by undergoing the moult and regrowth in one go, the period is shortened to the minimum. The majority of species of geese and ducks are completely flightless for about four weeks. The smallest of the swans, the **Bewick's**, also takes no more than four weeks, while the larger **Whooper** takes five to six weeks. The **Mute Swan** has the longest flightless period of the wildfowl, up to seven weeks, but that is still a lot less than many small passerines take to complete their wing moult growing their feathers one by one.

It must be apparent that the divers, grebes, rails and wildfowl, as well as sharing the characteristic of simultaneous wing-feather moult, share a further common factor, that is to say their affinity with water. It is their ability to find both food and security either on or very close to the water that makes it practical for these

A Mute Swan in moult. The normally slightly raised main flight feathers of the wings have been shed, as they are each summer, so that a new set can grow. The tail stands out much more than usual and the whole silhouette of the bird is changed.

groups of birds to adopt the strategy of rapid wing-feather moult combined though it necessarily is with temporary flightlessness.

Among the wildfowl, the aquatic feeders, particularly the ducks, can stay on water throughout the period. They can mostly feed as normal and can avoid danger in the form of predators by swimming away from the shore or by diving. Those species which feed mainly on land, especially the swans and the geese, either increase the proportion of aquatic plants they eat, or continue to feed on terrestrial plants but always within easy reach of water. Thus, during their moult **Mute** and **Whooper Swans** feed mostly on vegetation which is growing in water and only rarely feed on land, but some of the goose species will graze on the shores close to a lake, reservoir or river. They have the ability, described in the previous chapter (pages 33–5), to run when required. If danger threatens, they make at high speed for the nearest water and then usually bunch together and swim well out from the shore to wait until the danger has passed.

Completing the wing moult as quickly as possible has obvious advantages in terms of energy-saving and in reducing the period of even slightly impaired flight to the bare minimum, but carries enormous risks. Running, swimming and diving may not be enough to escape every kind of danger, and, just as importantly, they may not be sufficient to allow the bird to obtain all the food it requires. The choice of moult locality is all important.

A single moult of the wing feathers is normal for all the wildfowl with the exception of some of the stifftails, which undergo such a moult twice in the year, once in spring before the breeding season and then again afterwards. The introduced North American **Ruddy Duck** does this, although the native **White-headed Duck** does not. No theory seems to have been put forward as to why Ruddy Ducks need to undergo the energy-taxing full moult twice a year.

Catching geese

Escape from most enemies may be satisfactorily solved by swimming and diving, but flightless geese on the land are at considerable risk from foxes and other land predators. They are in even more danger from man, who discovered many centuries ago that it was possible to catch geese while they were flightless. In some places, particularly in the Arctic, this was a traditional and well-organized means of obtaining substantial numbers of birds which could provide a valuable food resource for the lean winter period to come. In central Iceland, stone corrals were built hundreds of years ago in the main breeding area of the **Pink-footed Goose** into which the flightless birds were driven. On Kolguev Island off the coast of north-west Russia, a British naturalist watched about 3300 **Brent Geese** being caught and killed in a single drive in the summer of 1894. The Inuit of northern Canada, Alaska and north-eastern Russia also traditionally caught flightless geese, and in a few places probably still do although the need for food is no longer so vital.

More recently, scientists have taken over the techniques of catching flightless geese and adapted them for the purpose of marking the birds with leg rings and then releasing them, in order to study migration, breeding habits and other aspects of their biology. Every summer, thousands of geese of several different species, including **Snow**, **Whitefront**, **Canada**, **Brent** and **Barnacle**, are caught for ringing in different areas of the North American, European or Russian Arctic.

Even allowing for a fair number of failures when the geese defeat the catchers, it is a perhaps surprisingly simple matter to round up flightless geese into a corral of netting. There are two major variations on the basic technique. One involves putting up the corral in a suitable place and then bringing the birds to it. The other involves surrounding the birds first and then putting up a corral and driving them into it. These two methods evolved in response to different behaviour by different species, and both were used by native peoples catching geese for food and are still used for ringing today.

The first method usually tends to catch larger numbers of birds and originally required a considerable team of people. A corral or pen of netting on stakes is first erected at a convenient site, perhaps not too far from a village or camp. Wings of netting extending on each side increase the catching potential by acting as guide walls to the running birds. If erecting the pen causes disturbance to the geese, a few days may elapse before the goose drive begins. The idea is to surround as many geese as possible, which might mean the catchers encircling an area of several square kilometres of tundra and then gradually walking in towards the pen herding the geese before them.

Species such as the **Snow Goose** normally feed in marshland and wet tundra, where lakes or even rivers may be scarce. On being alarmed, these birds will run long distances but will not necessarily make for open water. The skill of the catchers lies in heading the groups of geese in the right direction so that they gradually combine into larger and larger flocks as they approach the pen. The last stage of the drive requires considerable skill on the part of the catchers in ensuring that the geese are slowed to a walk as they reach the pen and do not charge through it wasting all the effort.

Nowadays the hard work, and the requirement for large numbers of people, is taken out of the process by the use of a helicopter. Once the pen is in position, the helicopter takes off and flies in a wide circle to get behind as many geese as possible. With its far superior speed it can act like an airborne sheepdog, gradually pushing the geese in the direction of the pen. A skilled pilot can shepherd the geese right into the pen. Although a helicopter is expensive to operate, there is a balancing saving in the number of people required.

The second method of rounding up flightless geese normally catches only one flock at a time and relies on the fact that feeding flocks of several species, including **Barnacles** and **Whitefronts,** will, when alarmed, make for the nearest water and then swim tightly bunched together. The intending catchers therefore approach a feeding flock and let them run on to the water, but then hold them there by having people around the other side of a small pool or using boats on a larger one. The pen with its guide walls is then erected close to the water's edge and the geese are driven off the water and into the pen, which is closed behind them. Boats or wading people are normally sufficient to persuade the geese to go in the right direction.

The above description may sound as if the whole operation is comparatively straightforward and indeed it usually is, even though it is sometimes surprising how easily the birds will allow themselves to be driven into a pen of netting which they have watched being erected. On the other hand, not all geese are as amenable to being driven in this way as, for example, Barnacle and Canada Geese seem to be. **Greylag Geese**, in particular, seem to have evolved a behavioural pattern which successfully defeats the majority of round-up attempts. Instead of allowing themselves to be herded into the waiting pen, the flock on the water begins to lose its cohesion as the geese begin to spread out, then scatter and finally dive to avoid the people or boats behind them, a most frustrating occurrence.

Quite why it is only the Greylag among the geese which has developed this skill at avoiding capture is difficult to know. One possible theory is that this species, which breeds widely through the temperate zone of Europe and Asia, has been in much closer contact with man for far longer than the Arctic-breeding species, and so has had time to evolve an escape mechanism in response to attempts at rounding up flightless birds. Whatever the reason, while rounding up flightless geese in the Arctic, or indeed the introduced **Canada Geese** of Britain and other parts of Europe, can be guaranteed to work almost every time, there have been remarkably few successful round-ups of **Greylag Geese** and very many failures, including when attempting to catch the introduced feral flocks living in Britain or the Netherlands.

Moult migrations

Apart from safety from predators, or from people trying to catch them for food or for scientific study, flightless wildfowl must have access to sufficient food in the place where they have gone flightless. They cannot fly off to find somewhere else if it runs short. For this reason, some species or populations undertake 'moult migrations' in order to reach areas which can sustain them safely during the moult period. One of the best-known of these takes up to 100,000 **Shelducks** from most of Britain and Ireland, the Netherlands, Germany, Denmark and the

countries around the Baltic to the vast sandflats of the German Waddensee in the south-east corner of the North Sea. Here this vast assemblage of birds can find both complete security and abundant supplies of the small, sand-living molluscs and other invertebrates which are their main food.

So suitable is this area for Shelducks that the birds that go there include the majority of the breeding adults, only a small number staying back with the broods of young. The latter amalgamate into larger crèches, thus releasing a proportion of the parent birds from their caring duties. The main moult migration takes place in June and early July and the peak moult

Young Shelduck in a crèche, accompanied by two adults. The majority of breeding adults desert their young when they are about two to three weeks old and set off for the moulting grounds. The broods of young combine into crèches, looked after by a very few adults, who may or may not have their own young in the crèche.

period is in late July and August. The birds do not then return to very promptly, however. The Waddensee continues to be able to support these huge numbers well into the autumn so that it is often October or November before they commence their migration back to their breeding grounds.

Many of the geese nesting in northern latitudes also have moult migrations. Because the breeding adults remain with their broods, however, the migration involves mainly the immature non-breeders (one- and two-year-old birds) as well as any adults which have failed early in the nesting stage. These birds move away from the nesting areas, often going to the north, where there may be suitable areas of grazing and marshy ground but no breeding birds.

Moult migrations also occur among the ducks, some of them over comparatively short distances. For example, flocks of moulting **Red-breasted Mergansers** gather in shallow sealochs and sheltered sounds in western Scotland, probably having come no more than 50 km or less.

The main purpose of the moult migration is to find an area of relative safety with abundant food which will last throughout the length of the flightless period. It has the secondary effect of taking a large segment of the population away from the breeding grounds, leaving the food supplies there for the benefit of the young of the year.

Added risks

There have been recorded instances of mass mortality of wildfowl during the moulting period, when the food supply in a given area, for some reason, became inadequate. At least fifty **Mute Swans** out of a flock of about 400 moulting at Abberton Reservoir in Essex, in the summer of 1958 died when a period particularly cold weather and high water levels led to a much poorer growth of aquatic plants than usual. The swans were flightless and so were unable to move elsewhere to find a new food supply or gain access to adjacent pastures.

One final aspect of becoming flightless is that it deprives the parent bird, particularly a swan or a goose which continues to look after its brood of young, of some of its ability to stand up to potential predators on its young. it may be able to look after itself, but it is also vital that it can also defend its cygnets or goslings. The members of breeding pairs of most swans and geese at least partially solve this problem by not moulting at quite the same time. One of the pair, usually although not invariably the female, moults its wing feathers while the young are only a week or two old, and then, anything from a few days to two weeks later, the other of the pair, normally the male, moults in turn. By the time the male has regained its powers of flight, the young will be nearly fledged so that the whole family will be able to fly at the same time.

Identification problems

The dabbling ducks and some of the seaducks become much harder to identify during the period of the wing moult because, prior to shedding their wing feathers, they moult their body feathers into their 'eclipse' plumage, which is often more like the female's and serves to render the flightless bird less conspicuous than when it is in its breeding finery. Apart from this difference, it is difficult to tell when a swimming duck is flightless or not. Geese and swans can more obviously be seen to be flightless, because the absence of the main wing feathers alters their shape. The smooth arch running from the base of the neck to the tip of the tail is lost. The tail becomes much more conspicuous and can be seen rising up at a sharp angle from the line of the back.

Perhaps not surprisingly, moulting wildfowl often become much less approachable than when they can fly. Many dabbling ducks skulk in dense vegetation such as reedbeds. Geese stay close to water and quickly run on to it when alarmed. Another obvious behavioural trait is that the birds spend a lot of time preening, helping the old feathers to come out and the new ones to shed their waxy sheaths. It is tempting to think that it is a pretty itchy time for them and that there must be quite a lot of discomfort involved which preening must help to alleviate.

Losing the power of flight is a potentially traumatic occurrence for a bird. Regaining it should be as great a relief.

SOCIAL BEHAVIOUR

The majority of wildfowl species are gregarious, occurring in flocks except during the comparatively short period of the breeding season. For some the family structure is also important, the young birds staying with their parents for many months, learning from them and being guarded by them. The behaviour of the individuals and family groups within a flock of wildfowl is as revealing as the behaviour of the flock itself.

FLOCKING

The importance for wildfowl of being in flocks has already been mentioned briefly. By being a member of a flock, the individual gains three major benefits concerned with avoidance of predators, feeding and pairing. For the majority of bird species there are probably few, if any, disadvantages in flocking, but it is an interesting fact that the principal quarry species for man – wildfowl, waders and gamebirds – are those that live in flocks and so give an increased opportunity for trapping, shooting or capture which man has long exploited.

Safety in numbers is a good maxim. Except for a short period during the breeding season, all the wildfowl species normally occur in flocks throughout the year. Some species, notably the **Common Eider** and several of the geese, also nest in colonies, while most of the others form flocks very quickly after nesting has ended. An exception is the **Mute Swan**, pairs of which may stay all year on their nesting territory, although these form only a tiny part of the total population, which otherwise lives in flocks.

A flock is rarely a random assemblage of birds. A small flock is very likely to be made up of related individuals which have bred in the same area and are now migrating and wintering together. At some stage, several small flocks may amalgamate into larger ones, allowing, among other things, mixing of genes as birds from different breeding areas pair up.

Among the geese and swans, flocks are made up largely of pairs and family parties, which reflects the social behaviour of these species. Pairs are generally formed for life and the parent birds look after their young for several months, even up to a year after hatching. This prolonged period of parental care is of great benefit to the young, which are both physically guarded when they are small and also shown by example the migration routes to follow and the best staging and wintering areas.

Most geese and swans are highly traditional in their use of nesting, feeding and roosting areas within their range, the same birds returning year after year to the same places. Such a tradition makes a lot of sense, as the birds will be familiar with the terrain and thus waste as little time as possible in finding a nest site, roost or good feeding locality. Clearly, this tradition will be instilled in the young birds during the period they stay with their parents and so passed to succeeding generations.

It was thought for a long time that the longest a family party stayed together was until the completion of the spring migration back to the nesting grounds, where the young geese or swans, not mature enough to breed until their second, third or even fourth year, would move away and form summering flocks on their own. Any further contact between these immature birds and their parents was believed to be purely accidental. Recent studies of individually identifiable birds have shown, however, that this is not always the case. The **Bewick's Swans** at Slimbridge in Gloucestershire, which can be distinguished by the patterns of yellow and black on their bills, and **Greenland White-fronted Geese** in Scotland and Ireland, which have been caught and given leg rings or neck collars engraved with unique number and letter codes, have both been found to maintain closer associations between older, related birds than had been supposed. In certain circumstances the young apparently stay with their parents throughout the summer, while more usually they link up with the parents again after the breeding season is over, either prior to migration or back at the wintering site.

Although it appears to be a rare event, there are records of family parties which apparently failed to split up on arrival back at the breeding grounds and stayed together throughout the summer, reappearing on the wintering grounds still as a family. It is possible only to speculate why this may occur, but it seems always to be linked with a failure of the parents even to start to nest, which in turn may be associated with a shortage of food or perhaps a hormone imbalance, either of which could prevent them coming into breeding condition.

The more usual occurrence, of the young birds joining up again with their parents on migration or on the wintering grounds, is obviously made more possible by the strong tradition of using the same places each year, which the parents passed on to their young the previous year. The association between older young and parents seems not to be inhibited by the presence of new young of the year. Nor is it confined to a single further winter. One **Bewick's Swan** continued to associate with its parents for a total of five winters. 'Super-families' sometimes build up, comprising the adult pair, their young of the year, and additional young from two or more previous years.

There is a positive advantage for these enlarged families within a flock, which is that it enhances their position within that flock. Just as among farmyard hens there is a pecking order, with dominant birds able to lord it over subdominant birds and so obtain first go at the food, so too in flocks of swans and geese there is a hierarchy of dominance. Rather than being among individual birds or pairs as in the farmyard, here it is among families and pairs and individuals. Thus, a family party of two

adults and four cygnets or goslings will normally be dominant over a family with only three or two young, which in turn will be dominant over a family with a single young or a pair without any. At the bottom of the pile come unpaired birds and, in particular, orphan youngsters that have become separated from the rest of their family and so have lost all their status.

A small group of White-fronted Geese keep a respectful distance from each other. Although gregarious and staying in flocks, except when nesting, a pair or a family party of Whitefronts prefer to keep a small, mobile territory around themselves while they feed. Aggressive encounters are quite common in feeding flocks as the birds attempt to maintain their spacing.

It has been shown that dominant birds enjoy not only better feeding than subdominant birds but also better survival and better breeding success. So, the best way to get on if you are a swan or a goose is to be part of a large family. It follows that a super-family is going to be best of all. It is of benefit to the parents to have more birds attached to their family, while the one- and two-year-old immatures greatly enhance their status within the flock by being part of a family instead of being on their own or just in newly-formed pairs.

While the geese and swans have this family structure within flocks, this is not so for any of the ducks. With rare exceptions, only the female parent looks after the brood of young. In the dabbling ducks, this period of parental care lasts until about the time the young fledge, which is usually from five to seven weeks. Then the female deserts them, and so far as is known there is no further acknowledged contact between them, even if they join the same flock thereafter. The females of diving ducks and seaducks tend to abandon their young even before they have fledged. For example, young **Tufted Duck** are left to fend for themselves at about four weeks of age, although it will be a further week or two before they are fledged. The young of **Ruddy** and **White-headed Ducks** are the most independent of all, sometimes virtually rearing themselves from a few days old, although others may be accompanied by the female for the first two or three weeks of their seven-week fledging period.

This lack of family structure also involves the adults, because the pair-bond of ducks is normally severed as soon as females have laid their eggs and incubation has begun. Males move away from the vicinity of the nesting place and in the case of most species gather in flocks for the post-breeding moult. Once this is completed, the males of migratory species begin to head towards their winter quarters, well ahead of the females, which have to complete the breeding cycle and then moult in turn before they migrate.

A consequence of this difference between the sexes in timing of migration is that most flocks of ducks contain a considerable imbalance of males and females. This is true for the dabbling ducks, although sometimes not very obviously, and is most exaggerated in the diving ducks, such as the **Tufted, Pochard** and **Scaup**, and in some seaducks, such as **Goldeneye** and **Common Scoter**. Flocks with up to 80 per cent of one sex have been recorded in some areas.

Although the males set off on migration first and so could, in theory, more easily go further south than the later-arriving females, in practice the reverse is true. This is because the males fly only as far as they need, arriving first and staying in the more northerly parts of the winter range. When the females and young birds arrive and find these localities already full of males, they move on further south until they reach less densely occupied sites. Thus, it is normal to find a high proportion of males in the north of the range and for females to predominate in the south. As the winter progresses, these positions may be changed, as it will be the males which are the more likely to be affected by severe weather and be forced to move further south.

Feeding benefits of flocking

The structure of a feeding flock of geese can be quite easy to observe, although naturally a good vantage point is desirable. A car makes a good hide and a position a little above the flock so that one can look down on it is also helpful. It is easiest if the young of the species are readily distinguished from the adults, which is true only of **White-fronted** and **Brent Geese**. The young and old of other species, such as **Pinkfoot**, **Greylag** and **Barnacle**, are much harder to tell apart, although it can be done in good conditions, the young being generally duller and browner.

The first observations should be of the leading edge of the flock; geese normally feed into wind and having landed in a field will move steadily in that direction. Young geese walk and feed faster than adults, and the leading edge of the flock will contain a higher proportion of young birds than further back into the flock. As the young move towards the leading edge, so their parents get pulled along with them; it is very much a case of the young leading the family group, rather than one or other of the adults doing so as might be expected.

Assuming the differences between young and old geese are clear, then it should be possible to see that the birds within the flock are, in fact, in family groups, each few young with their attached male and female parents. There are no goose species in which the male and female are different from each other in plumage, although with practice it is possible to tell which is which of a pair because the male is always larger than his mate, even if only slightly. There is quite a lot of overlap between males and females in measurements and weights, but it seems to be an almost universal rule that a male will have a mate which is smaller than he is, a difference that shows up in the field.

Following a family of geese as they feed will reveal a number of facets of their behaviour as they move through the flock and what happens when they encounter other geese. Much of the time it may all seem very peaceful, but every so often there will be an aggressive encounter. This may be no more than a goose rushing towards another, its head held low and outstretched,

chivvying it out of the way. If the chivvied bird is subordinate to the aggressor, then it moves out of the way and the matter is resolved. Sometimes, however, an encounter takes place in which neither family is dominant over the other. In these circumstances, a full confrontation may develop.

There is considerable similarity in the aggressive behaviour among the different species, although some, perhaps particularly the **Greylag** and **Canada Geese,** have a more complex system of threatening postures than, for example, the **Barnacle Goose.** At a fairly low level of intensity, the birds may stretch their necks upwards, or pump them up and down. If this does not produce the desired effect, the wings are brought into play, being flapped vigorously while the bird is in an upright posture. As tempers rise further, one bird may dart at another and grab some feathers in its bill. This may induce flight, in which case the aggressor will sometimes hang on and the two birds will run rapidly through the flock, one trying to shake off the other.

Actual fights among birds of a feeding flock are rare, although they are commoner among nesting birds. The most usual outcome of encounters between evenly matched families is

Two family parties of Whooper Swans display vigorously at each
other, arguing over a boundary to a feeding or roosting area.
Within a flock of swans a pecking order develops with larger
families normally dominant over smaller ones and able to drive them
away. When two equal-sized families have a dispute it often results
in much display and loud calling though only rarely to actual
physical contact.

a 'shouting' match, the birds facing each other, necks stretched
out, wings often held open, while all the time uttering loud calls.
Such a display between families of **Bewick's** or **Whooper Swans** is
a very noisy affair, the bugling calls ringing out across the water.

If neither side backs down, the encounter usually ends quite
abruptly, the birds turning away from each other to indulge in
some preening or to commence feeding again. No one has won,
and the same two families may well have similar encounters in
future until the matter is settled one way or the other.

Encounters between pairs and single birds are comparatively
rare, because both are fairly low down in the pecking order. The
bottom-of-the-order orphan youngster will generally stay out of

trouble near the back of the flock. If it finds itself too close to a family, it will often move out of the way before any threat is issued. A temporarily separated young goose, however, which has perhaps landed some distance from the rest of its family as they flew in to join a flock, has to run the gauntlet of pecks and rushes from other geese as it makes its way as quickly as it possibly can to rejoin its siblings and parents.

The principal reason for such aggressive displays is the defence of a feeding area. Feeding swans and geese do not have fixed winter territories, unlike many other species, of which the obvious example is the Robin in one's garden. Instead, they defend a small space around themselves as they feed within a flock, a family acting as a unit in this respect. As they move, so the 'territory' moves with them. If their food is evenly spread throughout the feeding area, as for example in the autumn in a lush grass field, then every goose has much the same opportunity to feed and there is little need for aggression between them. If, though, the food is patchy, as it can be on a harvested field of corn or potatoes, or in the somewhat artificial surroundings of a town-park lake or on a nature reserve where food is provided, then the dominant birds will seek first to take over and then to defend the best patches. This has the effect of pushing the subdominant birds to the less good feeding areas.

The advantages to birds within a flock of obtaining the best food are obvious. Family parties, pulled to the front by their rapidly walking and feeding youngsters, are also exploiting the best food. A flock of grazing geese removes a considerable part of the grass sward each time it visits a pasture, and while even densely flocking species such as **Brent** and **Barnacle Geese** do not remove every blade evenly as they go, in the manner of lawnmower, nevertheless there are clearly going to be more blades of grass available for the birds in the leading edge of a flock of several thousand geese than there will be for those that are forced into bringing up the rear.

The reason why young geese make for the edges of a feeding flock seems to be that they are less efficient feeders than older birds, not able so easily to select the best, most nutritious blades of grass. They thus seek out the best available food, i.e. the longest, densest grass or the greatest concentrations of spilt grain in a stubble field, which are always in front of the feeding flock. In this way they compensate for their less efficient feeding by increasing the chances that each peck will produce high-quality food.

As well as this advantage, the mere fact of being in a flock actually leads to better feeding opportunities for all. It has been shown that geese are capable of assessing feeding opportunities for themselves by watching the behaviour of other geese. A goose finding little to feed on will walk steadily, pecking intermittently. On the other hand, if it moves into an area of high-density or high-quality food, its walking rate will slow down while its pecking rate may increase, signs very obvious to other geese.

Most of the examples so far drawn in this chapter concern geese, mainly because they are among the easiest species to observe. In exactly the same way as described for geese, however, a duck that is dabbling for food will spend much longer in an area where surface seeds or invertebrates are abundant but swim or paddle much more where they are more scattered. Equally, a diving duck that has found a good food source under the water will dive repeatedly in the same spot, whereas one that is finding little will move between dives.

If we can observe such differences in feeding behaviour, it is certain that others of the same species can do so also and are capable of learning from what they observe. If one bird spots that another has, by its behaviour, found a better food resource than its own, then it will move to take advantage for itself. If the food resource is a large one, perhaps a completely different field, then no problems arise, but if it is merely a small patch of high-quality food then aggressive encounters may ensue as the more dominant birds either defend or try to take over the patch.

It is known that flying geese can assess the feeding potential of a field by observing the feeding behaviour of any birds on the ground, their density and their speed of movement. It can be assumed that this is true for all species, whether feeding on land or water. The converse is also true, in that new arrivals will avoid areas where the food has been depleted, thus sparing themselves wasted time and energy looking for food that is not there.

One other advantage of feeding in flocks has already been mentioned in an earlier chapter, namely the benefits that accrue from communal feeding, as undertaken by, for example, **Shoveler** or **Red-breasted Mergansers**.

Anti-predator benefits

A flock of birds is more likely to spot approaching danger because there are many pairs of eyes on the lookout, thus greatly reducing the chances of a sneak attack by, say, a fox. If one looks at a feeding flock of swans or geese, the majority will have their heads down, feeding, but there will always be some heads raised, the birds looking about them. The latter are probably scanning for predators and other danger, although they may also be assessing the feeding potential as just described.

It has been suggested that these birds are 'sentinels', carrying out a guarding function deliberately on behalf of the flock. Behaviour of this kind is known for a few species of birds, notably some of the babblers, where particular individuals take it in turns to stand guard while the rest of the group feeds. However, such an organized system has not been shown for the geese. Rather, each goose has a pattern of feeding bouts interspersed with short spells when it looks around. There are, though, marked differences in the frequency with which individuals take time off feeding to keep watch. The variation depends upon their social status within the flock.

Within a family party of swans or geese it is the adult male which spends most time with its head up in the alert position. This is most marked on the breeding grounds, when his vigilance allows not only the growing young but also the female, which will have lost weight during the incubation period, to feed uninterruptedly. When the family arrives on the wintering grounds, the male is still more vigilant, but the female and to a lesser extent the young do now raise their heads and look around more than before. Within just a pair it is always the male which is the more vigilant.

Increased awareness of approaching danger is certainly a major benefit of being a member of a flock, and predation on flocking birds has been shown to be less than it is on solitary individuals. There is not a perfect relationship between increasing flock size and decreasing predation, because very large concentrations of birds may actually attract more predators to the vicinity. Also, in very large, dense flocks, an individual's view of a predator may be obscured by its neighbours. It is even possible that birds may get in each other's way as they try to manoeuvre at close quarters in rapid flight.

When a Peregrine comes flying over a lake, estuary or marsh, the typical behaviour of the ducks, as well as of waders and gulls, that were feeding there is to rise suddenly into the air and to wheel and turn in their flocks. The smaller, more agile ducks, such as **Teal**, are capable of high-speed synchronized flight,

A dense flock of Wigeon on a saltmarsh. Most wildfowl are highly gregarious during the winter months. Flocking conveys anti-predator advantages and may help in the search for food sources. Wigeon are tolerant and will feed very close together without bickering.

wheeling and turning together in the same way as flocks of waders or Starlings. Even the larger geese are capable of such antics, although necessarily at a slower pace and with more space between individuals. Even so, collisions can occur.

As the Peregrine rarely strikes a bird on the ground or water, it might be thought that the birds would be safer if they stayed where they were. The reaction to flee is clearly the overriding one and it does have some anti-predator advantages. A sudden eruption of a mass of birds which then turn and wheel together will have the effect of confusing the predator and actually reducing its chances of making a successful kill.

The typical strategy of a Peregrine is to try to pick out an individual bird, which it will then stoop on from a height or pursue in more level flight. If it is suddenly confronted by a great congregation of possible targets, it may well fail to identify a single one for capture. Additionally, when threatened by danger, birds give out loud alarm calls. Geese do this very noisily and so do some of the ducks, particularly **Teal** and **Wigeon**. It is thought that the calls, rather than drawing attention to the individual, alert the predator to the fact that it has already been spotted and so its chances of making a kill have already been reduced.

Benefits of mixed-species flocks

Although flocks of a single species of wildfowl are perhaps the normal occurrence, there are many situations in which flocks of two or more species are found. This is perhaps most true of the dabbling and diving ducks, where on a lake or marsh one might encounter **Mallard, Teal, Wigeon, Pintail** and **Gadwall**, or **Tufted Duck** and **Pochard**, all swimming and feeding together. The mixing is probably not random as there is never complete overlap between feeding niches, as explained in the chapter on Feeding Behaviour and Habits. **Bewick's** and **Whooper Swans** occur together at many haunts, while mixed flocks of geese are common in some areas, for example **Pinkfeet** and **Greylags** in parts of Scotland, or **Whitefronts** and **Red-breasted Geese** in Romania, sharing both roosts and feeding areas.

Such mixed flocks lead to a better exploitation of the available food resource and may also, by increasing the overall numbers, have a beneficial anti-predator effect. Essentially, though, these are flocks of different species that have come together in one spot. If circumstances change, they will separate; the linkage is only temporary. The occurrence of scattered individuals of one species in flocks of another has a rather different basis with the advantage solely to the individual.

The benefits of being in a flock, as discussed above, are significant enough to make it important that straying individuals do find a flock as quickly as possible. Moreover, if a flock of the right species is not available somewhere in the vicinity because the stray bird has moved out of its normal range, then it is clear that such benefits are paramount and outweigh the disadvantages of being in a flock that is not of one's own species.

It is relatively common in some areas to find one or two individuals of one species of wildfowl in flocks of another species. Birdwatchers have long realized this and will spend long periods scanning through flocks of geese or ducks looking for the 'stranger', the rare bird that has wandered away from its usual haunts. Almost all the occurrences of the rare **Lesser White-fronted Goose** in western Europe, away from its south-eastern European wintering range, have been in flocks of other species, especially **White-fronted Geese**. The same is true for the even rarer **Red-breasted Goose**, which invariably is seen with either **Whitefronts** or **Brent**; this is not an accidental choice as these two species are the commonest geese breeding within its own nesting range in Arctic Russia and so the most likely for it to encounter.

A number of North American duck species regularly find their way across the Atlantic and most are spotted on this side among flocks of European ducks, often of a closely related species. Thus, **American Wigeon** frequently consort with European **Wigeon**, American **Green-winged Teal** with European **Teal**, and **Ring-necked Ducks** with **Tufted Ducks**. These strays have found the nearest equivalent to a flock of their own kind.

ROOSTING

The need for sleep has to be fitted in with the need for food. Not all wildfowl sleep at night. Some feed then and sleep during the day, while others have their feeding and sleeping habits determined by the tide. Regardless of timing, however, all wildfowl must sleep and all must be safe from predators and other dangers while they do so. Some wildfowl may roost where they feed, but others make regular flights between roosting and feeding sites, often of many kilometres.

The majority of wildfowl feed by touch and so can feed as readily in the dark as in daylight. All the diving species do so, other than those, such as the fish-eating **Red-breasted Merganser** and **Goosander**, which actively pursue prey. Up-ending birds, such as swans and dabbling ducks, also obtain their food by touch. Most dabbling ducks, although they may need sight to

locate good concentrations of food, do not then need to see what they are actually sieving from the water. Only the grazing birds, the geese and the **Wigeon**, need to see what they are pecking at, although even they can manage in very low light levels, for example, under the moon when night feeding regularly occurs for up to a week either side of full moon.

The first requirement of a roost is that it is safe, both from predators and from other forms of danger, such as shooters. Water is an obvious barrier to such threats, and virtually all wildfowl roost either on water or on islands in lakes or estuaries. A degree of shelter is also sought by some species, and lakes surrounded by trees are often preferred to more exposed sites. Species roosting on the sea, however, seem able to cope with very rough conditions although avoid breaking waves if they can.

Ducks that are feeding on water generally remain where they are throughout the 24-hour period, alternating bouts of feeding and resting, the latter including sleep. There is not necessarily a set pattern for these activities and some species seem to behave differently at different sites. Thus, **Tufted Duck** on some waters feed almost exclusively during the day, spending up to 70 per cent of their time feeding and the remaining hours preening, bathing and resting. At others, they seem to be much more nocturnal, at any rate judging by the much greater proportion of daylight hours spent sleeping.

Pochard are more often nocturnal feeders, becoming active just before dusk, with a major feeding bout in the first part of the night, a rest period around midnight and then further feeding towards dawn. The daytime is spent sleeping. **Ferruginous Duck**, too, feed at night but in some places just as often during the day, interspersed with periods of sleep.

When dabbling ducks are feeding on water they tend to be more diurnal, feeding around the edges of the water during the day, then moving out into the middle of the lake or reservoir for the night, although if there is a convenient island they will sit out on the shore of that. When feeding away from water, perhaps on spilled grain on stubble fields, they are much more likely to be nocturnal, feeding in the safety of the darkness when neither foxes nor shooters can see them and roosting during the day on a nearby lake or estuary. Their most vulnerable time

A flock of Barnacle Geese drop down to their roost on the saltings while other flocks fly further up the estuary. A secure night-time roost free from predators, and also from shooters, is a prime requirement of geese and the existence of such a roost within range of feeding grounds will be a major factor in their distribution.

is when they are flying to and from the roost at dusk and dawn, when shooters lie in wait for them under their flight lines.

Wildfowl-shooting is also directed at geese when they are flying, but the danger from predators is much less for these larger birds with their habit of feeding out in the open in large fields and they clearly feel safe enough to feed during the day and roost at night. Most geese will also feed at night when there is enough light, particularly under the moon. This is often forced upon them during the middle of the winter, when the days are barely long enough to allow them to feed sufficiently. A **Barnacle Goose** needs to feed for about seven hours a day in order to maintain its weight, an indication among other things of the poor levels of nutrition in grass. Consequently, in areas where midwinter days are no longer than seven hours, the geese take the opportunity provided by moonlit nights of extending their feeding time. In some places, geese feed on fields close to built-up areas where the reflected light from street lighting provides sufficient illumination for them. **Pinkfeet** regularly do this around Formby in Lancashire.

Estuarine species of wildfowl which feed below the high-water mark, such as **Shelduck**, **Wigeon** and **Brent Goose**, have their feeding and sleeping regimes entirely controlled by the tide, forced into a cycle of just over twelve hours, which therefore steadily moves in relation to the 24-hour cycle of day and night. Over the course of a fortnight, these birds will find themselves feeding at every hour of the day and night, having to avoid the attentions of predators and shooters alike.

Seaducks frequently make short movements between their feeding place and roosting place, even though these may be on the same general stretch of sea. The normal pattern seems to be that the birds have to feed in comparatively shallow water, and therefore often fairly close inshore, but prefer to be further away from the coast when roosting. This makes sense in keeping them from drifting too close to land while resting at night.

Birds roosting at the heads of estuaries and sealochs also face the problem of drifting around at night. Many geese roost in such places, and throughout each night the area will change from exposed sand and mudflats to being underwater. The birds tend to land in the same area each evening regardless of the tidal state, although if there is an area of saltmarsh adjacent to the mudflats they will often land on that if the tide is in, but then swim out on to the water as it gets dark. If they get drifted too far during the night, they will make short flights to regain a better position.

The timing of leaving and returning to the roost is governed by the amount of daylight. An overcast, grey morning will result in a much later flight than if it dawns bright and clear. There is also a correlation with temperature, the birds seeming much more reluctant to leave when it is cold. Other factors which affect the timing include whether or not the birds have managed to feed under the moon that night or just how well they fed the previous day. In any event, a departure from a roost, whether of ducks or geese, is usually an extended affair, lasting an hour or more for roosts of a few thousand birds.

Within a roosting flock there is much individual variation in timing of flight. Studies involving birds marked with radio transmitters have shown that over a period of few days, although the flock as a whole was leaving the roost over about the same period each morning, individuals within it were behaving differently on successive days.

After a day or night spent feeding on land, the roost provides the returning birds with opportunities for drinking, bathing and preening, as well as sleeping. These topics will be explored in detail in a later chapter. The need for water, not often present in a dry and dusty stubble field, sometimes drives the geese or ducks to fly back to the roost in the middle of the day for a short refreshment period.

BREEDING BEHAVIOUR

There can be few more thrilling or evocative sounds than the yodelling calls of a male **Long-tailed Duck** as he courts his mate. They have a melodious richness that make this an unlikely sound to emanate from a duck. They are accompanied by posturing and bowing, or a dramatic flight in which the male towers into the air before dropping vertically on stiff wings to land with a mighty splash beside his mate. Other wildfowl, too, indulge in elaborate or noisy displays designed first to form and then to reinforce the pair-bond between the sexes.

Once the pair has formed, the next vital stage is copulation. Here again there are special displays, usually although not always initiated by the male, to ensure that both birds of the pair are simultaneously ready for mating. Almost all wildfowl mate on the water, so making this even more of a balancing act than it is for the majority of birds, which mate on land or on a perch. It is therefore vital that both are equally prepared by mutual displays. Immediately after copulation, further, usually brief, displays set the seal on the now-physical bond between the pair.

Males of most species defend their mates against rivals and, in the swans and geese, a successful defence is followed by a triumph ceremony in which the male, and the female, celebrate the victory in a display which further reinforces the pair-bond between them. This is perhaps the more necessary in these species, which pair for life, than it is in the ducks, where the pair-bond lasts only for the one season.

Some species require a nesting territory, while others breed in colonies. A nest-site has to be chosen and a nest built (both mainly or exclusively the female's duty). Parental care, from incubation and nest defence, through fledging and beyond, is shared by both parents in the swans and geese, but is undertaken by the female alone in the ducks.

COURTSHIP AND COPULATORY BEHAVIOUR

It is important that the female does not interpret the first approaches of a male as aggression, and some of the displays are carefully judged so as not to give this wrong impression. The fairly uniformly coloured swans and geese rely on voice as much as display, but the brightly coloured males of many of the duck species use their displays to show off their plumage to best effect as they try to persuade a female to become their partner.

It can be quite difficult to see all the full rituals of the courtship and other behaviour of wildfowl, although the members of a pair of **Mute Swans** do not hide what they are doing. Some of the detail of such displays is perhaps best observed with captive birds, in zoos and waterfowl collections, where displaying birds can be quite a feature in the late winter and spring. On the other hand, some elements of pair-formation or courtship display can frequently be observed among wild flocks, many species beginning their pair-forming behaviour as early as the autumn, and carrying on with it throughout the winter. This is especially common among most of the ducks.

Swans

The **Mute Swan** is one of the most graceful of birds and its displays are no exception. Courtship between birds seeking a mate for the first time will begin in the autumn, usually of their second year, or sometimes not until their third. The two birds swim together, facing each other on the water, breasts almost touching, their neck feathers fluffed up and their wings slightly raised (*see* overleaf). Then they slowly turn their heads from side to side, as if making alternate eye contact has a special significance. This greeting ceremony will continue throughout their paired life together, used whenever the two swans have been apart, even for a short while. As well as being the main ritual to bring a pair together, it obviously has a strong reinforcing effect on the pair-bond of a species which pairs for life.

A pair of Mute Swans, once well established, will adopt a nesting territory, which is defended vigorously against other swans. The male is the more aggressive of the pair and will swim strongly across the water towards a potential rival, its wings half raised and its head and neck laid back between them. Every feather is raised and this gives the effect of a much larger bird. This display, known as busking (*see* overleaf), is often enough to scare off another swan; if not, then an attack is launched, usually by flying low over the water in pursuit. As the defending male lands back on the water he slaps the surface with his feet, adding an audible warning to his rapid approach. If on land, the male opens his wings and holds them out, slightly bent at the joint so that the outer feathers point down to the ground. This posture again has the effect of making the bird look larger and more impressive to its rival which it seeks to drive away.

Assuming all goes well and the intruder is driven off, the male returns to his mate and they immediately perform the triumph ceremony, a celebration of victory. Both birds raise their wings and fluff their feathers, similar to the busking posture of the threatening male, and then lift their chins in the air and simultaneously utter a curious snoring-like call. There seems little doubt that the intruder represents a threat to the pair and that this display has an important part to play in demonstrating to each of the pair that the threat is over and the integrity of the pair, vital for successful breeding, remains intact.

The pre-copulatory behaviour of Mute Swans is identical in both sexes, but is probably always initiated by the male. The birds swim close together, often facing but also side by side, and then alternately dip their heads into the water and bring them out again before preening and rubbing their back and flanks. This activity may continue for several minutes, sometimes coming to

A pair of Mute Swans court each other, their neck feathers ruffled and wings slightly raised as they turn their heads from side to side. This display will continue through their paired life as a greeting ceremony.

A male Mute Swan 'busking', raising his wings to make himself look much larger while he steams towards a rival in order to drive him off the nesting territory. The word probably comes from an old sailing term meaning to cruise or to beat about.

an end with the birds moving away and feeding, but if all goes well it increases in intensity and becomes more and more synchronized. If synchrony does not occur, the intensity wanes and the pair drifts apart unconsummated. More usually, however, synchronization is followed by the male moving towards the female and pushing himself up on top of her body, seizing the feathers on the back of her head in his bill to help maintain his position and balance. The female lowers herself into the water as he mounts, until all that can be seen of her is her head and back, and her raised tail.

For all birds copulation is very quick, lasting only seconds, and this is true for the swans. As soon as the male has slipped off, both birds give a muted trumpeting call and then meet breast to breast and rise up out of the water, paddling hard with their feet, extending their necks upwards. They point their bills up, then down, then side to side, before subsiding into the water and beginning to bathe and preen. The tails are usually wagged vigorously at this point, presumably as a comfort movement. It is a dramatic moment performed by these magnificent birds.

The displays of the **Whooper** and the **Bewick's Swans**, are essentially similar to each other. Courtship behaviour is much like that of the Mute Swan, the birds swimming breast to breast and turning their heads from side to side, the neck feathers fluffed. The triumph ceremony, though, is much more vigorous than in the Mute Swan and is accompanied by loud bugling calls as the birds face each other, with wings outspread, and bend and stretch their necks at an angle of about 45 degrees. The calls alternate between the pair in a superb duet – the calls of a Whooper Swan can carry a kilometre or more – but gradually synchronize until the two are calling in unison, blaring out their triumph.

Analysis of this pattern shows a remarkable degree of audio control by the birds. The calls gradually increase in duration, from about a tenth of a second to half a second, the lead bird making the change and the second bird following very quickly in lengthening its call. The male is probably usually the lead bird:

there are conflicting reports as to whether he always produces the lower note of the pair, although being larger, he should.

The successful seeing-off of a rival, which precedes the triumph display, is achieved by performing a similar loud-calling ritual with the added threat of moving rapidly in the rival's direction. If there is a stand-off between two evenly matched birds, they will raise their wings fully and point their heads downwards, bills almost touching the ground if on land, or underwater if swimming.

Prior to copulation, the Whooper and Bewick's display is less elaborate than that of the Mute, confined to mutual head-dipping lasting only a few seconds before the male mounts. Immediately afterwards, the male spreads his wings, the female usually although not always follows suit, and the two swans call as they rise up in the water, turn quickly and then settle down to preening.

The pair of Canada Geese on the right see off an intruder. All the birds are calling, while the middle bird, the male of the pair, is making a rush towards the intruder, its head and body held low in a threatening posture. On successfully driving the third bird away it will return to its mate and both will take part in a triumph display.

Geese

The pairing display among the different species of goose does not seem to vary greatly, although very detailed studies have been confined to only a few of the species, mainly the **Greylag** and the **Canada Goose,** and then mostly by observing captive birds. There is no reason to suppose that geese in captivity behave very differently from those in the wild state, but there are some potential constraints which have to be taken into account. The most obvious is if the captive birds are pinioned and unable to fly. There is also often less space in which to perform and, more importantly, a much smaller choice of potential mate. Without observations of captive geese, however, we would probably know and understand much less about their behaviour. The following description refers mostly to **Greylag Geese.**

The male initiates courtship by approaching a female with his neck bent and his head tucked back on his body, bill tip touching his breast. A goose with his bill pointed at another bird is threatening it and this naturally has to be avoided in the first stages of courtship, otherwise the female is most unlikely to respond to his overtures. The next stage is that the male begins to defend his chosen female even before she has shown much, if any, interest in him although she at least tolerates his presence.

The male stays fairly close to the female but rushes at any other male which comes too close. The bill this time is pointed directly at the rival and the neck is held out stiffly at an angle. In intense threat the neck feathers are raised and vibrated, which, in species like the Greylag, greatly enhances the furrows which spiral around the neck. If the male is successful in seeing off the other goose, he hastens back to his female and goes into a triumph display as if to boast of his success.

The threat displays of other geese are generally similar to those of the Greylag, but with the **Canada Goose,** for example, the bird rushes forward with its head held close to the ground, the whole body and neck lowered to permit this. The bill is usually open and the bird is often cackling loudly.

The triumph display of geese is very similar to the aggressive display the male has just been carrying out, but instead of directing his bill at the female, which would have quite the wrong effect, the male stands to one side of her pointing past her flank. Furthermore, instead of the silent threat that he has just carried out, he now calls loudly, with long resonant notes interspersed with shorter cackling calls. If she is now beginning to be interested she starts to respond, adopting the same head-forward stance, similarly pointing past and not at him, and calls back.

In a flock of geese, several males may be courting the same female and this sometimes results in the males running after each other through the flock, each trying to keep the others away from the female. Occasionally the males take flight, although this is a rare occurrence among geese, albeit regular among some kinds of ducks (*see* below). Another feature of encounters between groups of males is a vigorous and rapid flicking of the wings over the back, occasionally developing into fights.

It is interesting to note that a courting male does not always have to drive off another bird before returning to his female and 'showing off' to her. Many times, males have been observed rushing away from the female as if driving off a rival when in fact there was no other goose near. This does not, though, prevent him returning to her and displaying as vigorously as if he had genuinely got rid of a threat. This presumably allows an

A pair of Canada Geese copulating. Like virtually all wildfowl, the pair copulate on the water, the female half submerging while the male grasps her nape feathers in his bill as he mounts. The female lowers her wings and raises and twists her tail to facilitate contact between the cloacas.

isolated pair of geese to form a good pair even though the normally very important stimulus of other geese is not present.

A pair of geese cannot be considered to be formed until the female has responded to the male's triumph ceremony by displaying back to him and calling in her turn. Again she does not point directly at him, but the birds stand more or less facing but with their heads alongside each other. Once she has done so, then the pair will greet each other in this way after every time they have been apart. It is after this response by the female that the male will first attempt to initiate copulation, although it may be some time before he gets any kind of a response from the female who rejects these early advances.

Copulation initiation involves the male swimming towards his partner in a special attitude, with the tail held very high, fully exposing the white undertail-coverts, the neck bent so that the bill points towards the water. As the male nears the female he will begin head-dipping, but to start with the female will ignore him and he soon stops. Later she will join in the head-dipping although copulation may not occur until the nest is being built. In the latter case, the ceremony ends in vigorous bathing, but, if copulation proceeds, the female lowers her head and the male grasps the back of her neck and mounts, just as with the swans.

The post-copulatory display of geese is brief, both birds, although especially the male, stretching their heads and necks upwards while giving a short trumpeting call. Then both fall to bathing and preening. The **Canada** and **Barnacle Goose** males both raise their wings, often up to about half open, immediately after copulation, but the **Greylag** raises only its wingtips while the **Brent** keeps its wings fully closed.

Egyptian Goose and shelducks

As befits a species which has affinities with both the true geese and the ducks, the displays of the **Egyptian Goose** have elements relating to both. There is a distinct triumph display between the birds of a pair, after a rival has been driven off, but in other ways there are close similarities with the Shelduck (*see* below) and the ducks. In particular, the female plays some part in selecting a mate, rather than leaving the initiative to the male. She does this by inciting a male to attack other males, apparently selecting a male on the basis of his subsequent displays.

The wings are used in display more than they are with the geese, in particular being spread to show off the very bold black-and-white patterns of primaries and coverts, and also the bright green speculum which colours the rear of the secondaries.

The **Shelduck's** pairing displays are still not fully understood but it seems that the female may begin the process by carrying out what is known as inciting behaviour, something which is common to nearly all species of ducks. It is actually a threat display in which the female, while side on to the bird she is threatening, makes pointing movements with her head and bill at the bird. In courtship, however, while pointing at one bird she is actually trying to encourage another male to drive off the threatened bird for her (*see* overleaf). If he is prepared to do this, then the pair-bond is beginning to form. The attack takes the form of a low rush at the opponent, the head down, bill open, and wings raised. A retreating opponent will, by contrast, sleek its plumage and raise its head. If it stands its ground, however, a fight will usually ensue, with much thrashing of partly extended wings and jabbing with bills.

Shelducks hold territory during the breeding season, although the territory is around a feeding area and not the nest. While the female is incubating, the male stays in the feeding territory. When the female comes off the nest, which she will do about twice a day, she flies to the territory and is able to bathe and then feed under the watchful gaze of the male, who relieves her of the need to watch for predators or interloping Shelducks. The male has to defend the territory and does so by threat displays, including a kind of rotating, pumping movement of the head. At its most intense, his display involves rhythmic up-and-down movements of the whole body. These displays are also used by both birds of the pair when defending their small young, preventing other Shelducks from coming too close.

The triumph display between a pair of Shelducks is more subdued than in swans and geese. The pair members swim side by side and each bird raises the wing nearest the other and simulates preening behind it, before both dip their bills in unison and shake their heads. Lifting the wing in this manner has the effect of showing off the bold black-and-white patterning of the wings, an obviously important signal.

A feature of Shelduck display, as with that of several species of duck, is when groups of several males pursue a single female and the birds take to the air. These pursuit flights may involve up to eight or even more males following the lone female, which flies in circles as each male tries in turn to fly alongside her. There is much calling in flight, with the birds performing alternate rapid wing-beating and gliding. This type of display is most obvious in April and May, although it sometimes occurs earlier in the year.

The pursuit flight as described involves a number of males pursuing an unpaired female, each seeking to become accepted by her. Later in the spring, one or more males which have been unsuccessful in obtaining a mate may pursue a paired female. If her mate cannot keep them at bay, the female will take off pursued by all the males, including her mate, again accompanied by loud calling and rapid wing flapping.

Copulation is stimulated between the members of the pair in Shelducks by mutual head-dipping, as is the case with the swans and geese, and sometimes by shallow diving by both birds. The female signals that she is ready to mate by lying prone on the water, thus making it easier for the male to mount, which he usually precedes by lifting his wing and pretending to preen behind it, just as in the triumph display.

As soon as copulation is over, the female calls while the male, still holding the feathers at the back of her head, pulls her back,

The female Mallard is trying to persuade her mate, the bird on the left, through her inciting behaviour, to drive off the intruding male on the right. She does this by facing away from the intruder but poking her head and bill downwards and then sideways towards him. She simultaneously gives a series of rather querulous quacks as further encouragement to her mate.

as they both rotate slightly in the water. He then lets go and raises his head and tail, before joining the female in bathing and preening, which she commences the moment he lets go of her.

The various displays of the Ruddy Shelduck are quite similar to the above, with minor variations, the female again taking the lead in selecting a partner.

Mallard

The best-studied among all of the ducks is the **Mallard**, and it is also by far the easiest to observe, whether on an open lake or marsh or on a pond in the middle of town or city park, where this highly successful bird is plentiful. A complete description of all the different displays would be very lengthy and so will be considerably shortened here, although without omitting too much of substance. Other species of dabbling duck have broadly similar displays, with some of the major variations outlined below. There are similarities, too, in the displays of diving ducks and seaducks, although the overlap is less. By dealing with one species in some detail, and highlighting some of the differences shown by the others, it is hoped to convey an overall picture of

the complex, yet enthralling, variety of displays that ducks exhibit during their courtship. There is no substitute for watching them oneself and every opportunity to do so should be taken.

The behaviour which will lead to the establishment of mated pairs begins among groups of males and females as early as October–November and continues throughout the winter, stopping only in the coldest weather or at times of food shortage. Initially, groups of males indulge in communal displays, swimming together while the females stay on the periphery. The males go through a number of elaborate and somewhat ritualized postures including tail-wagging, flicking their heads and then more major displays, which involve dipping their bill tips in the water and then suddenly flicking bill and head up in the air, producing a fine spray of water droplets, followed by a simultaneous lifting of the front and rear ends out of the water (known to behavioural scientists as the 'head-up-tail-up' display).

All the time, each male within the group of displaying males is trying to get close to a female, swimming alongside her, presenting himself to her, trying to attract her attention. The displaying males are giving the females the opportunity to select what they see as the best mate for themselves. As well as the physical displays, the males call during them, giving a variety of grunts and whistles, none of them very loud.

The courtship continues with a male swimming in front of a female and trying to lead her away from the rest of the flock. He does this by lowering his head and neck as he swims away or alternatively holds his head erect, bill pointing away from the female so as not to threaten her, and then sleeks the feathers on the back of his head, which produces a noticeable darker patch against the glossy green. If this fails to impress, he may shake his head from side to side or even jump out of the water briefly.

The female, once she has selected a male, begins to follow him but must now try to shake off the attentions of all the other males. She does this with her inciting display (*see* previous page). She swims alongside her partner and pokes her head and bill sideways and downwards towards his rivals, giving voice to a rapid series of rather querulous quacks. She is showing her disapproval of the other males and at the same time trying to persuade her chosen male to drive them away. He may or may not oblige but, if he does so, there is a whole range of ways he goes about it, from a version of the female's poking towards the rival with his bill to actual fighting, which is not uncommon among Mallard. The two males push breast to breast, pecking at each other's bill and feathers, which may end in each bird hanging on to the other while beating vigorously with its wings.

A female Mallard prepares for copulation by stretching herself on the water as the male continues to head pump prior to mounting, which he will do as soon as the female signifies her readiness by raising her tail and twisting it to one side.

The result of this is that the two birds usually rotate on the spot, accompanied by a great deal of splashing and thrashing of wings.

Mallard have a form of triumph ceremony between the pair after the male has successfully driven away a rival. It is not so obvious as in the geese or swans, but consists of the male returning to his mate lifting his chin and calling, while the female does a bit more inciting in the direction of the beaten foe.

Once the pair is formed, the bond is reinforced by mutual ceremonies, often involving mock preening. The birds are not actually indulging in feather care but use some of the movements to show off to each other. The most obvious of these is when the male lifts his wing on the side facing the female, exposing the coloured speculum. He then pokes his head behind it and runs his bill along the feathers, producing a slight but distinctive sound, which may be an important component of the display.

When pairs are separated they call a lot, clearly recognizing each other's voice. The male has a soft 'rab-rab' call, while the female utters what has been very well described as her 'decrescendo call', a series of around ten to fifteen loud quacks, beginning loud and decreasing in both volume and pitch. It is an unmistakable sound once heard.

Copulation between the duck and drake Mallard begins as early as February and continues through until egg-laying. It is another way in which the pair-bond is strengthened. It is initiated by either bird approaching the other and pumping its head up and down, from close to the water to full stretch. If the other bird is interested it joins in until the right moment has been reached, whereupon the female stretches out on the water, droops her wings slightly and raises her tail, allowing the male to mount. As he does so he grasps here nape.

Once copulation is completed, the male dismounts but keeps hold of the feathers on the back of the female's head with his bill and jerks his head back while rising half out of the water. Then he lets go, and while the female bathes and wing-flaps he swims rapidly around her, nodding his head, before he, too, bathes and wing-flaps, showing off his crown feathers.

There is an imbalance of the sexes in most flocks of Mallard, with males outnumbering females, because the latter suffer a higher mortality, particularly during the breeding season. So, after the Mallard have formed into pairs, usually by February or March, there is a surplus of unattached males. These continue to seek a mate, but can do so only by trying to detach a female from her mate. This produces the chasing flights.

Groups of males, perhaps only one or two, but sometimes up to fifteen or more, court the attention of a female. She incites her mate to see them off, but if he is unsuccessful, or perhaps not even present, she takes to the wing, closely pursued by the group of males. They fly around quite erratically and may settle for a short while and then take off again if the female is still being pestered and cannot find here mate.

Later in the season, flights occur which involve just the pair plus one other male. These are so characteristic of areas where several pairs of Mallard nest that they have been given the name of 'three-bird flights'. They occur when a female from one pair flies over the nesting area of another pair. The male rises to chase her off and, as she flies back to her own area, her mate comes up to follow. A flight can last for several hundred metres, before the chasing male gives up and returns to his own mate. The pursued female's mate does not interfere, even though the female is giving her inciting calls during the flight.

The three-bird flights serve the purpose of spacing out the nesting pairs, as the pursued female is discouraged from repeatedly flying over the area from which she was chased. Mallard do not defend large nesting territories as such, but more usually just a small area around the female, whether she is feeding or prospecting for a suitable nest site.

One final, and fairly dramatic, activity of the Mallard breeding season occurs when groups of males chase a lone female and attempt to rape her. This is commonest in the Mallard, although it occurs among other dabbling ducks and, to a much lesser extent, in some of the diving species. Mallard tend to nest more densely than other species, and this is undoubtedly a factor in the occurrence of forced copulation, as it is also called.

Once the female has laid her clutch of eggs and begun incubating them, the pair-bond breaks and the male leaves her to join in small flocks with other males. The groups pester females which come off the nest for short spells during incubation. The female no longer has a mate to defend her and may be attacked by up to twenty males. She then takes off, followed by all the males, trying to force her to the ground and rape her. It is difficult to explain this behaviour, because there is no longer much chance of the males being able to pass on their genes through her, which is the case earlier in the season when occasional rapes can occur, although they are usually prevented from happening by the female's mate. Whatever the reason, they are a normal part of Mallard behaviour. They are very occasionally fatal to the female and certainly somewhat distressing to watch.

Other dabbling ducks

The courtship and copulatory behaviour of the other dabbling ducks is the same, in its main essentials, as that of the Mallard. There are certain differences in emphasis, and certain postures of the courting males are commoner in some species than in others. The communal displays of the males perhaps vary the most. In the **Wigeon**, for example, the males are much more aggressive towards each other from an early stage, and some of the elaborate rituals of the male Mallard are largely absent. This is also true for the blue-winged ducks (**Garganey** and **Shoveler**). **Teal**, on the other hand, while extremely quarrelsome, with fights going on the whole time among the groups of males, nevertheless manage to have as many ritualized displays during communal courtship as the Mallard although these are much less easy to observe.

Copulation is stimulated in all species by mutual head-pumping, but after copulation not all males swim around their

Three male Pintail actively court a female. They are forcing their attentions on her, showing off their yellow and black undertails and the long tail streamers, as well as the bold chocolate and white head and neck. Eventually the female will select one of them and the pair will be formed.

female as in the Mallard, merely joining her in bathing and preening. Perhaps they have no need for pair-reinforcing displays.

Group flighting and chasing, three-bird flights and group rape occur in all species, but are limited in some by the very scattered nature of their nesting.

Diving ducks

The displays of the diving ducks are less elaborate than the equivalent ones of the dabbling ducks, which can be linked with the much duller plumage of the males. They are also less prone to fighting, the communal displays being more peaceable affairs. One of the more important displays of the males involves whipping the head back until it touches the middle of the back and then immediately bringing it forward again. This has been described as the 'head-throw' display and occurs not only in all the diving ducks but in the seaducks as well. It is accompanied by a soft whistling call. Other displays also involve the head, shaking it and flicking it. Male diving ducks can inflate the feathers of their neck and head and also have the ability to contract the pupil of the eye. This greatly enhances the size and conspicuousness of the iris, which is variously coloured red, orange or yellow in the different species.

The aim of these displays is the same: to attract the attention of a female. This is also done by swimming with a sharply kinked neck and by the male lying partly submerged in the water with the neck, head and bill stretched out flat along the water pointing at the female. These two displays are always accompanied by calling, a misture of soft whistles and croaks.

The interest of the female in one male is expressed by her inciting a selected male to see off others, as with dabbling ducks. Courtship flights and three-bird flights do occur but not commonly, even in places where the birds are nesting quite close together. They are most frequent in **Tufted Ducks.**

A pair of Tufted Duck copulating. The female has lowered herself in the water and the male is steadying himself by holding on to her nape feathers with his bill.

Pre-copulatory display consists of rhythmically dipping the bill in the water, rather than pumping the whole head and neck up and down, plus much false preening. As soon as the male has dismounted he gives a brief display, usually involving movements of the head and bill, before joining the female in bathing and preening. Some dive immediately after copulation.

Seaducks

The displays of the male seaducks are more vigorous and more elaborate than those of the diving ducks, designed to show off the bold plumage patterns of the majority of the males. Those of a few species will be used as examples.

A typical communal display group of **Common Eiders** consists of a single female and several males, perhaps up to ten,

Three male Common Eiders court a female. The head throw of the male is accompanied by loud coo-ing calls. The movements emphasise the bold black and white patterning of the birds, but also the softer, pastel pink of the breast and green on the nape.

occasionally more. The males perform a number of different displays accompanied by a variety of delightful soft cooing calls. The most obvious is a triple 'ah-OOO-ooo', which is given as the bird puffs out its chest, throws its head back until the bill is pointing vertically upwards, and then after a brief pause drops it back down again to the starting position. The sound from a group of calling birds carries far over the water. In other displays, still accompanied by cooing, the males point their bills down at the water, or turn their heads from side to side through 90 degrees, while keeping the neck stretched to its fullest extent.

Throughout all this displaying and cooing each male is also jockeying for position closest to the female, threatening and chasing the other males. All the birds within the group of birds are constantly on the move around each other. At times, the

A pair of Common Eiders preparing to copulate. The male approaches the female and displays to her, stretching his neck and pointing his bill forwards and upwards. She gradually lowers herself in the water and remains prone while he continues to display, sometimes for several minutes before he mounts.

female is jostled so much that she dives, immediately followed by all the males. On the surface, she begins, with bill pointing and low calls, to incite one particular male to chase off all the rest, and the pair has started to form. Both birds reinforce their bond with a series of different displays, including mock preening, flapping their wings, stretching their necks upwards, and dipping of bills in the water, accompanied by calls.

Some of these displays precede copulation. The male initiates matters by beginning to display at the female. She does not respond in kind but gradually adopts a prone position on the water. Instead of immediately mounting, as would occur in the dabbling and diving ducks, once the female has done this, the male will spend several more minutes displaying and cooing while swimming around her. There may not be any mutual pre-copulatory display in the Common Eider but there is still a need for the male to come to a peak of readiness.

Immediately after copulation, the male gives a brief display, usually rearing up out of the water and then swimming away with his neck stretched and his head turning from side to side. The female bathes and preens in the usual way.

The wonderful, wild calling of the male **Long-tailed Duck** was mentioned at the beginning of this chapter. No other ducks can make quite such rich and musical sounds. There are other ways, too, in which the courtship displays of this species are different.

With the Long-tailed Duck, there is only slight emphasis by communal displays of several males competing for the attentions of the females. It does occur but does not last very long, being supplanted by courtship on a one-to-one basis, each male courting a single female. First, however, the males need to sort themselves out and establish their rights in the area. This is carried out with much aggression among the males, involving chasing each other over and under the surface of the water, and taking to the air, calling all the while. The combined calls of a flock of males engaged in pursuits of this nature have been likened to the baying of hounds or even the distant sound of bagpipes, both stirring sounds, according to taste.

The next phase is communal, with several males gathering around each female. At this stage pursuit flights are common, with the female taking off followed by a cluster of three to six males. Both the males and the female call vigorously during the flights, which often zigzag low over the water.

When a single male begins to concentrate on just one female, he courts her by a series of displays, including stretching his head and neck up erect, calling loudly as he does so, and also shaking and tossing his head. Head-shaking produces alternate flashing of the black and the white parts of the head plumage, which must act as a very distinct signal to the female. The male Long-tailed Duck also has his long tail to show off, and he does this by suddenly arching his body so that the head and neck bend down towards the water while at the same time the rear end, with long tail streamers jutting into the sky, is lifted out and upwards and the feet are kicked backwards. A distinctive variation of the main courtship call is given as this is done.

All of this posturing and noise is initially greeted by the female with considerable hostility and she may decide to fly from the male, who normally pursues her, again giving tongue to his yodelling cries. As the courtship rises to a peak, she gradually

Two male Red-breasted Mergansers in different display postures.
The upper bird has jerked his head suddenly into this forward,
upward staring position, known as the 'Salute'. The lower bird has
moved on one stage to the well-described 'Curtsey'. During these
two displays, these otherwise relatively silent birds are giving voice
to a long metallic rattling series of calls.

reduces the level of her aggression and begins to tolerate the male near her. Eventually, she signifies her acceptance by lifting her chin at him as he displays. Once this has happened, the male greatly scales down the level of his courtship, both birds performing more subdued displays, including shaking and tossing their heads, and simultaneous bathing.

Unlike the Common Eider, both birds of the Longtail pair display prior to copulation, stretching their necks, head-shaking, bathing and lifting their chins. Finally, the female goes prone for the male, swimming towards him from a few metres away, passing him and turning to come back again. After copulation, the male performs a few more of the same displays while the female bathes vigorously beside him.

While many of the displays of the **scoter** species are broadly similar to those of other seaducks, there are some aspects peculiar to them. One of these is their habit of rushing over the water at a rival. The male scoter hunches his head back into his shoulders and then paddles furiously towards the offending bird. Actual fights seem to be very rare, so this aggressive rushing display obviously does the trick instead.

The male scoter also rushes at the female in courtship, but the posture is rather different. He crouches in the water, head tucked back but close to the surface. The back is then arched and the bird rushes forwards, only to stop very abruptly in a cloud of spray after travelling no more than a metre. The rushing is slower than when it is an aggressive act.

Scoters are not usually thought of as vocal birds, and certainly very little in the way of sound will be heard coming from a wintering flock. Once they begin to display, however, both males and females reveal a series of single-note piping calls that can carry far across the water on a still day. The wings of scoters also make a very distinctive whirring sound as they take off, although reducing to a quiet whistling in level flight. Part of the male's display includes taking off and flying low over the water for a few metres, giving perhaps eight or ten slow wing-flaps, producing this very audible noise, which is clearly part of the display as is the splashing landing.

Particularly distinctive displays of the male **Goldeneye** include a very dramatic leaning of the head back until it meets the middle of its back, then suddenly kicking out with the feet, which not only produces a large amount of spray but has the effect of lifting the rear end of the bird out of the water, while forcing the front end down. Simultaneously with the kick, the bird thrusts its neck and head vertically and gives out a loud and rasping double whistle, which can be heard a kilometre away.

Before they copulate, a pair of Goosanders indulge in a mutual ceremony of ritualized drinking, dipping their bills in the water and raising their heads, though not normally swallowing, but allowing the water to spill out. The female has lowered her crest and will soon go prone on the surface.

The **Red-breasted Merganser** and **Goosander** also have a display in which the bird appears to bow in the water by raising its rear end and depressing its front, but in this instance it lays its neck down on the water rather than vertically. The former species uses its crest in display, raising and lowering it. However, the effect is nothing like so dramatic as the crest-raising of the vagrant **Hooded Merganser**, which can totally transform its appearance as the slim black-and-white crest is suddenly unfolded to produce a white-centred, black-edged fan extending back from above the forehead and then as abruptly folded again.

Stifftails

Both **Ruddy Duck** and **White-headed Duck** males rush across the water in a hunched position, not unlike that of the scoters. They also stick both head and neck and tail vertically into the air, totally changing their normally round-backed silhouette, especially when the tail is also fanned. Male Ruddy Ducks court their females by beating their bill against their breast. There is an airsac here which, when inflated and beaten, produces a quite audible drumming sound. After four or five beats, the bird then presses its bill harder into the breast feathers, expelling lots of tiny bubbles which rise up around it accompanied by a further, harsher sound. This bubbling display is also performed by the male immediately after copulation.

Perching ducks

Mandarins have a well-developed communal courtship display but one which normally takes place in the early morning or evening, when the light is poor, or in the dense shade of overhanging trees. It may well be that these highly coloured and conspicuous birds find it necessary to be rather secretive about their display in this manner, because of the very obvious danger there must be of attracting the attention of predators.

Groups of males gather around one or more females and display to her, the female eventually selecting one of them as her mate. One common posture is for the male to stretch its neck to the fullest extent, fluffing the loose neck feathers and jerking the bill up and down. In another, the male, with crest raised to its fullest extent, swims alongside the female, dips his bill in the water, then passes the bill behind the 'sail' on the side nearest to the female. The sail is a highly modified inner wing feather. Male Mandarins, normally rather silent birds, have a range of whistles and nasal calls which they seem to reserve exclusively for courtship, so that a courting group is quite a noisy affair, another reason, perhaps, for performing in the half-light.

Copulation is initiated by the female swinging her head backwards and forwards while swimming in front of the male, then they both begin head-pumping while the female gradually goes prone on the water. The male displays briefly afterwards, but both then concentrate on bathing.

NESTING BEHAVIOUR

So far as is known, the female of all wildfowl species selects the nest-site. This may involve considerable prospecting in thick cover as a female duck looks for a well-hidden site, offering security from predators as well as freedom from flooding, or merely returning to last year's nest, as is common with a number of the geese as well as the swans.

It is also the female which builds the nest, except in the case of the swans, where the male helps to a greater or lesser extent. The first action of a ground-nesting duck is to smooth out a hollow by pressing her chest down on to the ground and slowly rotating. Having got this to her satisfaction, she will then line the depression with available material by standing in it and plucking at surrounding pieces of vegetation. No species of wildfowl is capable of carrying anything in its bill, so none brings in nest material from a distance in the way that so many birds do. The nest has to be constructed of what is within reach, and the presence of suitable vegetation will be an important factor in the choice of site for most ground-nesting species.

A number of species of duck nest in holes, including **Shelduck, Mandarin, Goldeneye, Smew** and, sometimes, the other sawbills. Where nests are in holes in trees, they are without nest material, or only the wood chips or whatever occurs in the chosen hole.

The swans, which build much more substantial nests than any other species, are able to increase the amount of available material to some extent by standing outside the area of the nest itself and reaching out for more pieces of vegetation. These are picked up and then tossed over the bird's shoulder in the direction of the nest. Exceptionally a swan may do this from a greater distance, moving the material three or four times in order to get it within reach of the nest. What it cannot do, however, is pick any of it up and walk with it. This limitation in their behaviour, common to all wildfowl, is linked with the fact that they do not need to carry food in their bills, as their young feed themselves from the day they hatch. The great majority of birds, which can walk, swim or fly with ease while carrying quite large objects in their bills, also need to be able to carry food to their young in the nest. Wildfowl have no need of this skill.

The nest of a swan is a large structure of grasses and rushes, 1–2 m across at the base and perhaps 50–80 cm high. Some of the geese build large nests, when nesting in fertile marshes with plenty of vegetation, but the arctic-nesting geese on the tundra have to be content with a hollow with little or no actual nest material, as do ducks nesting in such latitudes.

A common component of nearly all wildfowl nests is the down lining. This is plucked by the female from her belly during and immediately after egg-laying. The down is grown for the purpose by most species, being especially soft and often cryptically coloured. The effect of plucking the down is to leave bare patches of skin, which are placed against the eggs when the bird is incubating. Many species of bird have special bare areas on their undersides, devoid of feathers, called brood patches, but

the wildfowl produce theirs in this way, and once plucked the feathers immediately begin to regrow. The down acts as a fine insulating layer under the eggs, keeping them from the often cold and damp bottom of the nest. It is also pulled over the eggs when the female leaves the nest, helping both to keep the eggs warm and to conceal them from passing predators.

Incubation in wildfowl is undertaken exclusively by the female, although the male of some swans and geese will sit on the eggs during the laying period, which takes several days. However, he has not plucked any down and so has no bare areas of skin to help warm the eggs. The most he is doing is concealing them from predators. Incubation does not begin until all the eggs are laid, thus more or less guaranteeing that the eggs will all hatch at about the same time. This is very important for nidifugous species such as the wildfowl, where the young are going to be led from the nest within a few hours of hatching.

Most female wildfowl have one or two spells off the nest every 24 hours, usually in the early morning and late evening. They need to bathe, preen and feed. Swans, geese and shelducks can do this while being guarded by their mates and so free of the need to keep an eye open for predators or intruding males of their own species. Ducks have to fend for themselves, which tends to make periods off the nest quite brief. In some species, notably the **Common Eider**, the female will sit for longer spells, often days at a time, especially as the hatching date comes closer.

Swans and geese defend their nests vigorously against predators, flying at them, calling loudly, and doing their best to drive them away. Ducks can rarely challenge a predator successfully and so resort to other methods. The best-known of these is the distraction display. The female leaves the nest abruptly and flutters away across the ground or water, flapping her wings and quacking loudly. The aim is to distract the predator away from the nest and persuade it that there is an easy prey in this apparently damaged bird, which seems unable to fly.

Wildfowl nest in a great variety of sites, not all of them directly associated with water. The Goldeneye (top) uses the hole in a rotten tree and takes readily to nest-boxes. Shelduck frequently use old rabbit burrows as they cannot excavate holes themselves. The Mallard relies on screening vegetation and her camouflaged plumage to conceal her ground nest from predators. The large Mute Swan can defend itself and its nest and therefore has no need for concealment or coloured plumage. Red-breasted Mergansers prefer to be close to water and seek the concealing shelter of overhanging vegetation or a stream bank.

A pair of Mute Swans build their massive nest. The male, unable like all wildfowl to carry nest material in his bill, stands away from the nest, picks up pieces of vegetation and drops them over his shoulder to where the female can reach them.

A successful distraction by a female can lead a fox or a dog for several hundred metres before the bird suddenly flies up and makes a cautious way back to the nest, now safe from destruction.

Some female ducks, when flushed from the nest, defecate as they fly up, spraying the eggs with faeces. The incubating bird seems to forgo the need to defecate, connected no doubt with the very limited feeding that it is able to do. Perhaps as a result of this the faeces smell more strongly than usual, and indeed are particularly pungent and unpleasant. The effect this has on a potential predator is difficult to assess, but some mammalian predators seem to be put off by the stench, although it has no such effect on birds such as crows, which have a very poor sense of smell.

During incubation the female bird moves around quite a lot, shifting her position and those of the eggs, turning them with her bill and rearranging them from time to time. As hatching nears,

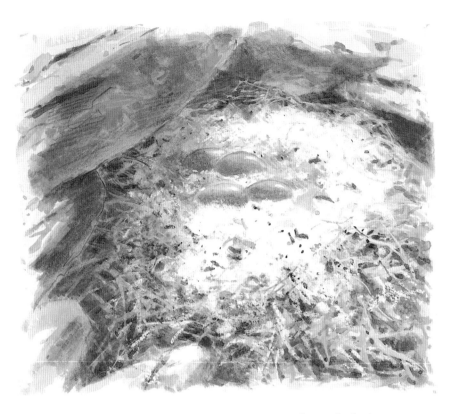

A Common Eider's nest. The olive-green eggs nestle in a bed of down plucked from the female's breast. It acts as insulation from the cold, damp ground, and will be pulled over the eggs to conceal them when the female is away feeding.

the chicks inside the eggs break through the membrane, their heads enter the airsac at the broad end of the egg and they then begin to breathe. They also begin to call, very faintly but distinctly, and are answered by the female, with soft notes, establishing a first and very important contact. Once hatched, young birds imprint upon the first moving object with which they are closely associated (they can imprint on humans if hatched artificially) and the visual imprinting is greatly reinforced by this additional aural contact just prior to hatching.

On hatching, a cygnet, gosling or duckling is a wet and bedraggled object, very different from the cartoon representation of an alert and fluffy youngster popping out of the shell, immediately able to run and swim. The first requirement is for warmth and shelter in order for the down plumes to dry and fluff out. There is also an urgent need for sleep, to recover from the not inconsiderable exertions of hatching. The female therefore broods her young for several hours, the period depending on the spread of hatching of the eggs and on the prevailing weather. She will delay leaving the nest in cold and wet weather.

It has been found that the most important time for imprinting by the young on their mother is the period when they are between about twelve and sixteen hours old. Very few broods leave the nest sooner than this. It is clearly vital to them that they spend this time in close visual, auditory and physical contact with their mother and with each other. The female **Mallard**, and probably other species, too, has a range of special calls which she utters while brooding her new-hatched young.

For those birds nesting on the ground, leaving the nest is a simple matter: the female merely walks off the nest, calling softly, and her brood follows her to the water. As explained earlier, the walk can be a long one in some cases, but the female keeps up

A female Mallard broods her young. For two or three weeks after the eggs have hatched, the female will provide shelter under her wings for her ducklings, both at night and during bad weather.

her calling, the young responding with soft contact calls or, if they lose contact, trying to attract their mother's attention with a high piping, distress call. This has the danger that it also attracts predators, but not being separated from the mother at this stage is of overriding importance to the young bird.

For those birds nesting in holes, often many metres above the ground, the female has to adopt a different strategy. To start with, the ducklings generally stay in the nest longer than do those in a ground nest. For the latter, not only are there no physical problems associated with leaving the nest, but they are more at risk from predators the longer they stay. On average, Mallard ducklings stay in hole nests for about 20–24 hours, with an extreme of 46 hours, compared with 14–16 hours in ground nests, and an extreme of 36 hours in bad weather.

The actual departure from a hole nest is clearly difficult for the young, the female needing to encourage them to take, literally, a leap into the unknown. **Goldeneye** regularly nest up to 5 m above the ground, while **Mallard** have been recorded as high as 10 m. **Barnacle Geese** in east Greenland nest on cliff ledges 20 m or more up vertical faces. All need to entice their young down from these heights. They do this by flying down to the ground and then calling in a particularly excited manner. The Goldeneye has a special call reserved for this time, which the ducklings clearly respond to. They crowd to the mouth of the hole and it is not too long before one jumps, or perhaps is pushed from behind, to be quickly followed by a steady stream as the remainder follow. If one stays back, it will almost certainly start distress-calling, which immediately attracts the attention of the female, who carries on calling until the nest is quiet. She does not fly back in to check if it is empty, though.

There is some dramatic film, which has been shown on television, of a pair of Barnacle Geese leading their young from a high cliff ledge, then down through some boulder scree to the grazing marshes in the valley floor. Both adults are making high-pitched, harsh calls, while the young respond with vigorous cheeping, especially when they get left behind or are out of sight of their parents. The nest is on a bare rock ledge, and the first jump is out into space and a fall to the rocks beneath. The young show some hesitation before leaping, but less than might be expected. Tests with goslings have shown that they have no fear of heights, in contrast to the young of many ground-nesting species, which instinctively draw back from the edge of a steep drop.

The loud calling of the adults is clearly essential to encourage the goslings to leave the cliff ledge but it has the drawback, shown very dramatically in the film, of attracting the attention of predators, in particular the Arctic Fox. It is the presence of foxes within the breeding range of the Barnacle Goose that forces the bird to seek inaccessible ledges for its nest. The adults rush at the fox, but fail to protect all their young from being seized.

In the Arctic, Barnacle Geese cannot use the cover of darkness to lead their young from the nest, but in fact nearly all wildfowl generally lead their young from the nest in the day, very rarely at night, and most often in the morning. The first requirement is to take them to a suitable feeding area, however near or far that may be. The young feed themselves from the outset but are wholly dependent on their parent or parents for protecting them from predators. They respond to an alarm call from their parents by swimming quickly towards them and bunching together.

For the first few weeks, the female will brood her young, coming out on to the shore and gathering them under her wings, for as long as they will fit there. This is very important while they are still down-covered, as they require the extra warmth she can give them at night, and protection from heavy rain.

The **Mute Swan** has the most sophisticated method of parental care, the adults carrying the cygnets, when small, on their backs. From the time they become active after hatching, the cygnets have a strong urge to climb. They board the adult from behind, in the gap between the tail and the tips of the folded wings, and then snuggle in under the wings. The Mute Swan holds its wings slightly arched, and this provides a considerable space for the cygnets. Although it is mainly the female which carries the cygnets, the male also does so occasionally, perhaps helping with a particularly large brood.

Carrying of the cygnets is commonplace for the first ten days of the cygnets' life, becoming less frequent thereafter as they get larger, although it has been recorded as late as six weeks. The parents do not actually help them up but do sometimes raise a leg under the clambering youngster, allowing it to get purchase from the heel. Once aboard, the cygnets sleep there, but it is usual to see one or more heads poking up between the wings at the front and providing one of the more attractive wildfowl pictures.

The cygnets of the Whooper and Bewick's Swans are never carried in this way. The cygnets lack the innate urge to climb of Mute Swan cygnets, nor do their parents have the 'brooding space' under the wings, which are held tight to the body.

The only other wildfowl that has been recorded carrying its young, and then only rarely, is the **Goosander**. On the few occasions it has been seen, the young were very small, as would have to be the case, as there would not be room for them when they were more than a few days old. The suggestion has been

A brood of young Mute Swans get a lift on their mother's back.
The cygnets have an instinct to climb when they are small. There is
plenty of room for them on the adult's broad back and within the
space created by the slightly arched wings. They are safe here from
predators, and can keep warm and dry.

made that as most Goosanders nest in holes, where there is little space, the newly hatched young would find themselves on their mother's back during their preliminary explorations. Also, as hole-nesters, they have the urge to climb, to leave the nest.

Once the brood of young is safely away from the nest and beginning to grow, they quickly develop a repertoire of calls which convey information to the parent and, if necessary, elicit the appropriate response. The calls are basically the same for all the wildfowl, especially the distress call, a shrill peeping, given with the head and neck stretched up, a regular, loud calling that clearly demands attention. When all is well, cygnets, goslings and ducklings issue a soft contact call, given when the bird is feeding or is exploring with its siblings in the close proximity of its parent or parents. When being brooded, or just dozing on the bank, the birds give forth soft trills, sometimes known as sleepy calls. The youngsters also greet each other and their parents by lifting their chins.

Comfort Behaviour

The care and maintenance of body and plumage, but especially the latter, are the constant concern of all birds. Under the general heading of comfort behaviour, this occupies the time of wildfowl second only to feeding. As discussed under flightlessness in the chapter on Flying, birds' feathers have a finite life and must be renewed at regular intervals. That life can be prolonged by paying due regard to such matters as cleanliness, the feather structure, its waterproofing, and keeping parasites to a minimum. The other external parts of a bird, its bill, legs and feet, eyes and nostrils, all require attention at frequent intervals. The skin, too, under all those feathers must be kept in healthy order. There are several different ways in which these vital matters are achieved.

BATHING

The principal purpose of bathing is to clean the plumage, not only of dirt, but also of parasites. It further helps a bird to cool down in hot weather, especially important for a female which has spent long summer hours incubating in some windless nest-site. Birds do not sweat but can lose some heat by panting.

It might be thought that a bird living on the water might not get very dirty. This is probably true of those species which are diving for their food, but surface feeders will get their head and neck coated with any scum that may be floating on the surface. Land feeders, particularly those swans and geese which dig for roots and tubers in soft ground, can get quite muddy around the bill and head, as can Shelducks after sifting molluscs from muddy estuaries. All of this must be cleaned off and not be allowed to clog the structure of the feather.

Parasites come in a number of different shapes and sizes. Some, such as lice and mites, feed on the actual feathers or on flakes of skin and blood. Others, including various forms of flies, fleas and ticks, are bloodsuckers. The lice and mites, and some of the louse-flies, normally live their entire life cycle on the bird, laying their eggs among the feathers, where the larvae also live and pupate. Fleas and ticks, on the other hand, have stages spent away from the bird, usually in the nest or on vegetation. A healthy bird can support a modest collection of these parasites without too much harm, although it is clearly advantageous to keep their numbers as small as it possibly can.

Bathing by wildfowl, whether swan, goose or duck, is a very vigorous affair, designed to get the water to have the maximum effect. Humans use soap to break down the surface tension of water and increase the cleaning effect. Birds have to rely on physical actions instead. Most wildfowl bathe when swimming, but some do so when standing in the shallows. Bathing usually starts by the bird ducking its head and neck into the water and then arching up and throwing the water over its back. The wings are brought into play, half-opened and shuffling splashily to bring more water over the body. At the same time the bird is opening up its plumage, holding the feathers erect and thereby increasing the space between them to allow the water to penetrate.

Some birds will stop at that, but others can be seen to half-dive as they bathe, the better to get the water over the top of their body. At their most active, bathing birds will roll on their sides and thrash vigorously with their wings, throwing up great sheets of spray (*see* page 2). They may even somersault forwards, awkwardly rolling head first, tail up, and emerging amid great shaking and flapping of the wings. Half-rising in the water while simultaneously flapping the wings hard against the water produces a spectacle and noise that can hardly be missed.

Sometimes a bathing goose or swan is joined by others in its family or flock and mass bathing ensues. The function of this is not very clear, but at its most spectacular several birds will be splashing and thrashing together, breaking off to chase each other, making short flights or even diving in the midst of the churned-up water. Young swans and geese do this frequently, one of the few occasions when these birds submerge fully.

DRYING

Wildfowl adopt the simplest possible method of drying their plumage, by shaking themselves. This can take the form of a wing shake, standing upright if on land or half-rising out of the water, and giving several hard, deliberate flaps of the wings. Then there is the body shake, beginning with a distinctive flicking of the head while at the same time the head and neck are rotated to and fro as the bill is pointed upwards. This movement is followed by a shaking of the entire body, again incorporating a rotary movement, accompanied by rapid fluffing up and sleeking down of the body feathers. The overall movement is very akin to that of a dog after a bath and the effect is much the same,

After a bath, a male Red-crested Pochard rises up in the water and gives several strong flaps of its wings and shakes its body in order to remove all surplus droplets from its plumage.

sending water droplets showering upwards and outwards on both sides. At the same time as the wing flap and body shake, the bird wags its tail firmly from side to side. All of these actions, as well as drying the bird, have the effect of settling the feathers back into place after the major disturbances of the bathing.

After a spell of heavy rain, most wildfowl will indulge in vigorous wing-flapping and even body-shaking in order to rid themselves of the raindrops settled on their plumage.

PREENING

The next stage of plumage care, after a good bathing sequence, is to preen the feathers and to apply preen oil to them. All birds require warm and waterproof plumage, but it is obviously of supreme importance for any bird living actually on water and often diving beneath the surface. Although preening always follows bathing, it also frequently takes place without the bird first getting thoroughly wet. When this happens, though, the bird may be seen dipping its bill in the water so that it is kept wet while working on the feathers.

The principal action of preening is to spread the preen oil via the bird's head and bill to restore the structure of the feathers. Each feather consists of a central shaft with side branches called barbs. Each barb has its own tinier branches or barbules. These are covered in minute hooks and grooves which interlock to give the feather its unified structure. However, as one knows, the hooks can be easily pulled apart and when this happens the feather becomes weaker, and can no longer resist the pressure of the air if it is a flight feather or so adequately exclude water or cold if it is a body plume. Preening must ensure that all the feathers are in immaculate condition.

A Bean Goose rubs the back of its head on its preen oil gland, situated above the base of the tail, prior to spreading the oil over the rest of its plumage. The oil preserves and cleans the feathers as well as waterproofing them.

The preen oil is a waxy secretion which comes from a gland located above the base of the tail. The bird nibbles at this, to stimulate secretion of the oil, and then rubs its chin and bill, or head if the neck is long enough, over the gland, transferring the oil to its feathers. The chin or head is then rubbed over the plumage elsewhere. The wings also get their oil, although the undersides sometimes present problems of access and bodily contortions are needed in order to reach every part.

Preen oil used to be thought to be purely a waterproofing agent, acting as a water-repellent, spread over the surface of the feathers, obviously of great importance to wildfowl. It has been analysed in detail in recent years and is known to have several other functions. The compound contains a mixture of fatty acids and alcohol and undoubtedly serves to maintain the flexibility of the feathers, acting on the keratin of which they are formed. It further has a cleaning effect. The preen oil of female **Mallard**, for example, has been shown to be toxic to fungi, although only during the nesting period of the year. When the bird is incubating she has much less time for feather care, while in the damp conditions of the nest minute fungi which can damage the feathers would flourish if nothing were done to prevent this.

Finally, there is some evidence that preen oil's smell, which is very strong in, for example, the petrels and shearwaters, has some function as a sexual attractant, related to pheromones. The preen oil of wildfowl species appears to have little or no smell, but some of the work suggesting a pheromonal role has been on geese.

Once the oil has been spread, and more is obtained at need, the bill is used in two ways when preening. Firstly, the bird nibbles at specific places on the feather, and strokes each feather either with the bill closed or by drawing the feather through the just-opened mandibles. Either way, the purpose is to pull the barbs and barbules into place and so make the hooks and grooves interlock. The actions also continue to spread the preen oil more evenly over all the surface feathers. The thick underlying downy plumage, which is thicker and more dense in wildfowl than in most other birds, is also preened and searched for parasites hiding there, but only the surface feathers require oiling.

Preening is usually done in sequence, with attention paid to different parts of the plumage in turn. Many wildfowl come

Preening actions of a Greylag Goose. Feathers on the chest are nibbled, while the tail feathers are drawn through the bill one by one, restoring their structure after bathing or damage. The wing feathers come in for special attention then finally the bird gives a vigorous all-over body shake.

ashore to preen, as it is obviously easier standing on firm ground to preen different areas of the body, such as the belly. The more aquatic species, however, will roll on their sides so that they can reach bits that would normally be difficult to reach underwater.

Preening further serves to rid the plumage of water left after bathing, particularly from the longer flight feathers in the wing.

SCRATCHING

Wildfowl lack the long, sharp claws of many birds and are handicapped by having webs between their toes. Nevertheless, scratching is another important component of body and feather care. In particular, the feet can be used to preen the head and neck, those vital parts of the bird which it cannot reach with its bill, but which certainly need as much care and attention.

The skin around the eye of this Canada Goose receives a delicate scratch from its toenail. This is almost the only exposed soft skin on a bird and wildfowl are prone to leeches attaching themselves to it.

Scratching while swimming is possible, although liable to involve quite a lot of splashing and therefore unwelcome further wetting. It is much easier if the bird is standing and can shift its weight on to one foot while lifting the other. A sudden itch or irritation will result in a brief scratch at any time, but, following bathing and drying, scratching forms a regular component of the preening sequence. Each foot is raised in turn and the head is lowered on that side to improve access, especially for the long-necked species which may, like the swans, also be short-legged.

The toes are obviously very useful in helping to dislodge parasites from among the feathers of the head. Many parasites concentrate in this region of the body for the good reason that they are out of reach of the questing bill.

CARE OF SOFT PARTS

The legs and feet of ground-feeding birds can get very muddy. I have seen geese feeding in a harvested potato field get huge lumps of sticky soil attached to the undersides of their feet, such that they pecked at them to try to rid themselves of the awkward burden. Obviously it does not take much to wash such encumbrances off, but there is an additional reason for needing clean legs and feet. These areas of bare skin are important to wildfowl for temperature regulation in hot weather, being the only substantial area where blood vessels reach the outside surface of the bird and heat can be lost through radiation.

The eyes are cleaned automatically by blinking, but parasites such as ticks and leeches sometimes attach themselves to the lids and are difficult to remove. The bird may try by scratching, but it needs to remove them before they take too strong a hold.

The nostrils, too, are a target for freshwater leeches and may also get clogged by dirt or mucus. The cleaning process involves the bird snorting or blowing down the nostrils while they are submerged in water. Such 'sneezing' is probably very effective and is often accompanied by vigorous head-shaking.

STRETCHING

There is nothing like a good stretch to finish a spell of body care, and wildfowl are no exception in doing this. There are two main types of stretching, with one wing or with both. The one-wing stretch is common to all birds and, although wildfowl sometimes do it when on the water, more usually they wait until they are standing. One wing is extended sideways and down-wards, sometimes also slightly backwards, until it is nearly or completely open. It is held there briefly before being folded away. The bird often then stretches the other wing in the same way. A common variant of the wing stretch is to combine it with a leg stretch. The leg on the same side as the wing (naturally!) is stretched out sideways underneath the wing.

The legs can also be stretched on their own, without any wing-stretching. This is most commonly done by a standing bird, but some species, notably the swans, will stretch out a leg and foot while swimming and then instead of returning it to the water will tuck it in the feathers of the flank, where it remains dry and warm. Swans will sometimes swim for quite a while with a foot lifted out of the water and the web spread out. This may be to dry it, but alternatively it may be using this method to rid itself of surplus heat as mentioned above.

The two-wing stretch is demonstrated by a Whooper Swan, half opening its wings while stretching forwards with its head and neck.

A Pink-footed Goose stretches out one wing and leg as a conclusion to a spell of preening. Sometimes only the wing is stretched.

The second way of stretching is to raise both wings above the back and simultaneously lean forwards and stretch out the head and neck. Again, the posture is held briefly before the bird folds its wings and stands normally.

RESTING AND SLEEPING

The commonest way in which wildfowl sleep is to tuck the head back over one shoulder, pushing the bill into the feathers. If the bird is standing on one leg, a very common posture, particularly for the swans, geese and dabbling ducks, then the head is always turned back on the same side as the lifted leg. The feathers into which the bill is tucked are the scapulars, which are long, overlapping plumes which bridge the gap between the wing and the body when the bird is flying. They form a neat and waterproof 'pocket' on the bird's flank.

Many birds, perhaps especially young ones, sleep sitting on the ground, perhaps easier on their leg muscles and tendons. Sometimes one sees a goose which has not tucked its head back but just left it resting on its breast, the bill tip gradually sinking until it touches the ground.

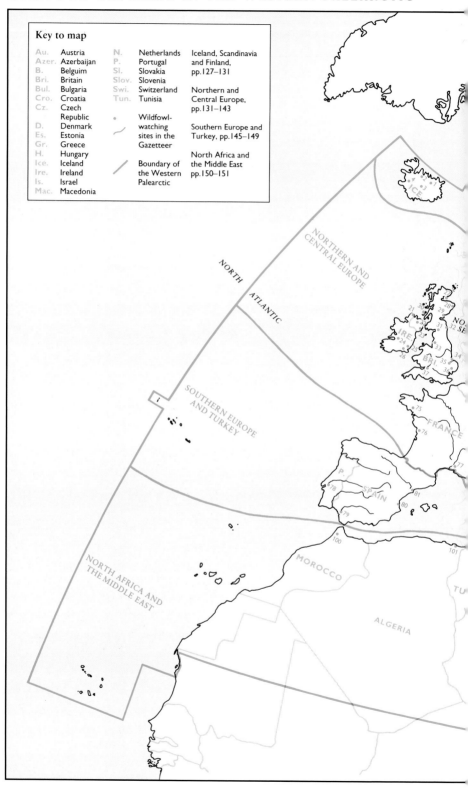

Key to map

Au.	Austria
Azer.	Azerbaijan
B.	Belguim
Bri.	Britain
Bul.	Bulgaria
Cro.	Croatia
Cz.	Czech Republic
D.	Denmark
Es.	Estonia
Gr.	Greece
H.	Hungary
Ice.	Iceland
Ire.	Ireland
Is.	Israel
Mac.	Macedonia

N.	Netherlands
P.	Portugal
Sl.	Slovakia
Slov.	Slovenia
Swi.	Switzerland
Tun.	Tunisia
•	Wildfowl-watching sites in the Gazetteer
╱	Boundary of the Western Palearctic

Iceland, Scandinavia and Finland, pp.127–131

Northern and Central Europe, pp.131–143

Southern Europe and Turkey, pp.145–149

North Africa and the Middle East pp.150–151

GAZETTEER

The spectacle of large numbers of wildfowl is one that has enormous appeal to birdwatchers and has also been shown, at the many reserves with visitor facilities, to be one that the general public, too, finds enthralling. The following list of sites includes many of the most important wildfowl haunts in the Western Palearctic. The numbers refer to the map on pages 124 and 125 and are arranged by country within four broad regions, in approximate north-to-south order. Selection of sites has been based on the criteria of overall abundance and, to some extent, variety of species. There is therefore an understandable bias towards those holding the largest numbers of wildfowl. There is space here only to mention a handful of the good wildfowl sites in each country, but it can be argued that these are the ones not to be missed. Attention should be paid to the timing of any visit. The great majority of sites listed hold their peak numbers during autumn or spring migration or during the winter months. Haunts where significant numbers of birds can be seen during the breeding season are relatively uncommon within the region, unless one travels into the Arctic.

ICELAND, SCANDINAVIA AND FINLAND

Iceland

This country is *the* breeding place for large numbers of wildfowl, including Whooper Swan, Greylag and Pink-footed Geese, Wigeon, Teal, Scaup, Tufted Duck and Common Scoter, which winter in north-west Europe, particularly in Britain and Ireland. These birds are not hard to find as wetlands, large and small, abound, although many of them can be reached only on foot or by four-wheel-drive vehicle.

1 Myvatn A total of about 10,000 pairs of sixteen different species of duck breeds on this large (4000 ha) shallow lake, both on its many islands and in the surrounding marshes with their numerous small pools. This is probably the greatest variety for any wetland in the Western Palearctic and includes almost all of Iceland's (and the region's) Barrow's Goldeneye (2500 birds all year), and Long-tailed Duck, Common Scoter, Wigeon, Tufted Duck and Scaup. Harlequin Ducks breed along the River Laxa and other streams.

2 Skógarfjördhur The river floodplain of this large northern valley holds many breeding wildfowl, including Greylag Geese, is an important moulting area for these as well as Whooper Swans, and is visited in spring by thousands of Barnacle Geese on their way to their breeding grounds in east Greenland.

3 Thjórsárver A large oasis of tundra and marsh in the centre of Iceland which is readily accessible only in late summer by four-wheel-drive vehicle. Still the principal breeding site for Pink-footed Geese (up to 10,000 pairs), but the recent population increase has meant that the species now breeds much more widely and can be seen in the upper reaches of many of the larger river valleys.

4 Borgarfjördhur-Straumfjördhur These west-coast fjords hold up to 180,000 moulting Common Eiders in late summer, while several thousand Light-bellied Brent and Greenland White-fronted Geese stop on passage, the latter feeding on the adjacent farmland.

Norway

Breeding wildfowl in Norway are generally scattered, with few haunts of any significance except in the case of Common Eiders, which are found, often in large numbers, all around the coasts. Greylags breed quite widely as far north as the Arctic Circle. Migrating swans and geese stop for periods, especially in the spring, while there are moulting and wintering concentrations of seaducks in many of the fjords.

5 Varangerfjord Renowned as the haunt of Steller's Eider (up to 10,000 in winter, 1000 in summer) and King Eider (up to 4000 in winter). These, with 6000 wintering Common Eiders and 1200 Long-tailed Ducks, make this a mecca for seaduck enthusiasts.

A pair of Greylag Geese indulge in a triumph ceremony. The male has probably just driven off an intruder and this mutual display which follows his successful return to his mate serves to strengthen the pair bond between them (see page 88).

The area around Vadsöy is probably the best site within this large fjord.

6 Tanafjord The wintering numbers of 4000 each of Common Eider and Long-tailed Duck and up to 800 King Eiders near the head of this fjord are dwarfed by the summer moulting concentration of over 25,000 Red-breasted Mergansers.

7 Vega Archipelago Virtually the whole of the Svalbard-breeding population of Barnacle Geese stays for most of May on some of the myriad small, grassy islands in this archipelago. Up to 250 pairs of Greylag Geese breed here and over 4000 gather to moult, as do up to 4500 Common Eiders. Several islands hold managed breeding colonies of the latter species.

8 Orlandet wetland complex A group of several wetlands near the mouth of the Trondheim Fjord which comprise the most important wildfowl area in central Norway with up to 7200 moulting Velvet Scoters, reducing to 3000 in winter, when 1000 Long-tailed Ducks and 4000 Eiders also occur.

Sweden

Considerable numbers of Whooper Swans, Greylag Geese and many duck species breed widely around the very numerous lakes and marshes in the north and centre of the country, while the southern marshes and coasts are important for passage wildfowl, some of which will stay through mild winters.

A Greylag Goose, Wigeon and Whooper Swans feeding on stubble well away from their natural habitat of water. The Greylag's bill evolved for plucking and digging, the Wigeon's for grazing and the Whooper's for probing in soft soil and vegetation. All three, have adapted to feeding on stubble, walking slowly along while picking up the individual spilt grains of wheat or barley (see pages 33–6).

9 Lake Tåkern Up to 3000 Mute Swans moult on this large shallow lake, while 200–300 Whooper Swans occur on passage. The surrounding farmland supports up to 40,000 Bean Geese in spring and autumn.

10 Lake Kävsjön This very large lake and associated bogland holds breeding Whooper Swans, Wigeon, Teal, Pintail, Shoveler, Garganey, Tufted Duck, Pochard and Goldeneye. Flocks of Whooper Swans and Bean Geese stop off here in spring and autumn.

11 Gotland Up to 1200 pairs of Barnacle Geese, of the Russian population, breed on small islands off the east coast of this much larger Baltic island. Thousands more stop off in autumn, together with Bewick's Swans, Greylag and Dark-bellied Brent Geese.

Finland

It is thought that there are about 60,000 lakes in Finland, which, together with vast areas of peatland with bog pools, support very large

A Canada Goose up-ends to reach underwater vegetation. Geese are not as expert at up-ending as swans and dabbling ducks and the effort usually shows in a lot of paddling and splashing with the feet (see page 18).

numbers of breeding Whooper Swans, Greylag Geese and a wide variety of dabbling ducks, diving ducks and seaducks. Parts of the south and south-west coast are also important. Cold conditions in winter mean that few wildfowl remain at that season.

12 Koitilaiskaira, Finnish Lapland A huge extent of peatland, streams and pools supporting over 5000 pairs of breeding waterbirds, including Whooper Swan, Bean Goose, Common and Velvet Scoters and Smew.

13 Kokemäenjoen suisto Up to 1000 pairs of ducks breed in the extensive reedbeds of this delta, including Wigeon, Teal, Pintail, Garganey,

Shoveler, Pochard, Tufted Duck and Goldeneye.

14 Gulf of Finland A vast complex of islands, channels and open sea holding tens of thousands of breeding and moulting Common Eiders. Huge numbers of seaducks gather there on migration prior to the last lap to their breeding grounds in Arctic Russia. Upwards of a million Long-tailed Ducks and 200,000 scoters have been estimated at peak times.

Denmark

The principal wildfowl concentrations in Denmark are of wintering swans, geese and ducks found in the many very large shallow fjords on the west coast and around the coast of Jutland in the north of the country. Not all are very accessible, but at the right tides at least some of the considerable flocks of swans and ducks will be found close to the seawalls. The geese feed on the mudflats and saltings and on inland farmland. The numbers given in the site accounts are averages of annual maxima over several years.

15 Ulvedybet and Nibe Bredning, Lim Fjord Almost in the middle of the north Jutland peninsula, these sites on the enormous tidal inlet of Lim Fjord include reed-swamp, saltings, mudflats and small islands. They hold 7000–10,000 Tufted Duck and Pochard, as well as very large numbers of Wigeon, Teal and Pintail. All three species of swan occur.

16 Mariager Fjord This fjord, on the east coast of Jutland, is a main haunt of the small Svalbard Light-bellied Brent Goose population, but also holds up to 5000 Mute Swans, 2000 Whoopers and 4000 Shelducks.

17 Nissum Fjord A large shallow sea inlet on the west coast of Denmark. Passage and wintering wildfowl include Light-bellied Brent Goose (up to 3000, or the majority of the Svalbard-breeding population), Mute, Whooper and Bewick's Swans (1000 or more of each species), Pink-footed Goose, Wigeon, Pintail, Goldeneye, Red-breasted Merganser and Goosander.

18 Stadil Fjord This shallow fjord and the adjacent farmland, lying to the south of Nissum Fjord, is autumn and spring home to 15,000–20,000 Pink-footed Geese, the greater part of the Svalbard-breeding population of this species. Several hundred Whooper and

Bewick's Swans also occur on passage, while many thousands of Teal, Mallard and Pintail pass through in autumn and stay on in mild winters.

19 Ringkøbing Fjord Mean annual peak counts at this very large fjord in north-west Denmark, together with the extensive marshes on the south side, include up to 30,000 Wigeon, over 10,000 each of Mallard, Pintail and Teal, at least 5000 Red-breasted Mergansers, 4000 Dark-bellied Brent (Russian population), 3000 Goldeneye and 1000 Shoveler.

20 Vadehavet (Danish Wadden Sea) The Wadden Sea is the name of the enormous area of mudflats, islets and bordering coastal flats that extends south and west along the coasts of Germany and the Netherlands. Passage and wintering wildfowl are abundant, with average peaks in excess of 80,000 Common Eiders, 25,000 Dark-bellied Brent Geese, 35,000 Shelduck, 54,000 Wigeon and 38,000 Mallard, with smaller (relatively speaking) numbers of many other species of ducks and geese.

NORTHERN AND CENTRAL EUROPE

The more westerly parts of Europe are mild enough in winter to hold major concentrations of wildfowl coming from their breeding grounds in the Arctic. Further east, the continental winters force birds further west and south. Several species breed in these temperate regions, in preference to further north, perhaps especially Mute Swan, Greylag Goose, Mallard and Shelduck, and also the introduced Mandarin and Ruddy Ducks.

Ireland

The mildness of Ireland's climate gives it the potential as an excellent wildfowl wintering area. Major wetlands are comparatively few, although minor ones abound. Peak numbers of many species occur in winters when cold weather strikes further east, particularly in Britain. Numbers of breeding wildfowl are relatively small.

21 Lough Swilly This large sea inlet has extensive intertidal areas and supports several hundred each of Whooper and Bewick's Swans, Greenland White-fronted and Light-bellied Brent Geese, and over 1000 Wigeon and Teal.

22 Lough Neagh and Lough Beg Up to 1000 pairs of Tufted Duck breed here, easily the largest concentration in the country. Several thousand winter, as do Pochard (up to 17,000), over 1000 each of Mute and Whooper Swans and up to 5000 Mallard.

23 Strangford Lough Over half the Greenland population of Light-bellied Brent Geese (up to 14,000) spend the autumn and early winter in this tidal inlet. Shelduck, Wigeon, Whooper Swan and Goldeneye are also numerous.

24 Shannon and Fergus Estuary The most important wildfowl haunt in western Ireland, the extensive area of mudflats, saltings and wet pastures attracting up to 1000 each of Shelduck, Wigeon, Teal and Shoveler as well as hundreds of Whooper Swans, Greylags, Light-bellied Brent and Scaup.

25 Wexford Harbour and Slobs The harbour acts as the main roost for up to 10,000 Greenland White-fronted Geese, 500 Bewick's Swans and 100 Whooper Swans, which feed by day on the North and South Slobs, extensive areas of reclaimed land. Large numbers of ducks occur here, too, especially Wigeon and Mallard.

26 Lady's Island and Tacumshin Lakes These two neighbouring coastal lagoons are both bordered by rich marshland. The more numerous wildfowl include all three swans, Wigeon, Teal, Shoveler and Scaup.

Britain

The numerous estuaries and firths provide excellent wintering sites for wildfowl in all but the severest winters. Many inland waters, natural and artificial, occur on the fertile lowland, and the larger ones support significant numbers of wintering birds. The most important breeding species are Mute Swan, Canada Goose and Mallard. There are small introduced populations of Egyptian Goose, Mandarin Duck and Ruddy Duck.

27 Moray Firth This complex of firths and inlets is winter home to several thousand Pink-footed and Greylag Geese, which roost on Loch Eye and the estuarine mudflats and feed in the surrounding farmland. Well over 20,000 Wigeon winter here, while in the outer part of the firth are some of the most important seaduck concentrations in the country, including up to 8000 Long-tailed Ducks, 4000 Common Scoters and 3000 Red-breasted Mergansers.

28 Loch of Strathbeg This coastal lake and adjoining marshes are a major haunt for passage and wintering Pink-footed (up to 30,000) and Greylag Geese (9500). Several hundred Whooper Swans also occur, as well as many dabbling and diving ducks.

Many birds rest by sitting down; this Barnacle Goose is also feeding a little, but its relaxed state is revealed by the slightly drooping wings (see page 123).

29 Loch Leven The islands in this large freshwater loch hold one of the most important concentrations of breeding duck in the country, including Wigeon, Mallard, Gadwall, Teal, Shoveler, Tufted Duck and Pochard. Up to 10,000 Pink-footed Geese and 4500 Tufted Duck winter, as do several hundred each of Whooper Swan, Shoveler and Gadwall.

30 Isle of Islay The concentration of wintering geese on this island, about 25,000 Barnacle and 10,000 Greenland White-fronted, is greater than any other in the country. Up to 1500 Scaup also winter, as well as smaller numbers of about twenty other species of wildfowl.

31 Solway Firth The entire Barnacle Goose population from Svalbard (about 12,000 birds) winters on the north side of the firth, mainly at Caerlaverock. Pink-footed Geese have topped 25,000, and the area is important for Pintail, Scaup, Greylag and Whooper Swan.

32 Lindisfarne Extensive mudflats and saltings are winter haunts for up to 3000 Light-bellied Brent and 25,000 to 40,000 Wigeon, while 3500 Common Eiders winter offshore, many of them breeding on the nearby Farne Islands.

33 Ribble Estuary and Martin Mere wildfowl reserve The estuary and reserve, an area of floods, marsh and wet pastures a few kilometres inland, between them support very large

133

numbers of Wigeon (up to 24,000), Mallard (4000), Teal (4500), Pintail (3500) and Pink-footed Geese (10,000). Several hundred Whooper and Bewick's Swans winter there, too.

34 The Wash Although known principally for its vast numbers of wintering waders, the Wash also holds up to 9000 Pink-footed Geese, 24,000 Dark-bellied Brent Geese, 23,000 Shelduck and 4500 Pintail.

35 Ouse Washes One of the most important inland wetlands in Britain, comprising wet pastures in which Mallard, Teal, Gadwall, Garganey, Pintail, Shoveler and Tufted Duck breed. The area is flooded in winter and is then home to thousands of swans (600 Mute, 6000 Bewick's and 500 Whooper), up to 40,000 Wigeon, 350 Gadwall, 3000 Teal, 7500 Mallard and 1800 Pintail.

36 Abberton Reservoir The many reservoirs in south-east England provide excellent wildfowl habitat. This is one of the best, with peak counts of 35,000 Wigeon, 400 Gadwall, 600 Shoveler, 3000 Pochard

A group of male Tufted Duck take off after a female. Courtship flights are a common feature of many species of duck. The female may have unsuccessfully incited her mate to chase away the other males and so, in order to escape their attentions, she takes off, followed by them all, including her mate (see page 97).

(during the summer moulting period) and 650 Goldeneye.

37 Upper Severn Estuary The Slimbridge wildfowl reserve near the head of the estuary has wintering White-fronted Geese (up to 4000) and Bewick's Swans (450). Mallard and Pochard are especially numerous among the many duck species to occur.

Russia

The northern tundra and taiga of this huge country provide the breeding grounds for several million wildfowl of a great many species. Those from the European part of Russia winter in north-west and southern Europe being joined by many birds from east of the continental divide of the Urals. Huge numbers also winter in the southern parts of Russia and the countries of the CIS, around the Black and Caspian Seas. There is space to mention only a handful of sites although it is worth noting that the numbers of birds at some of the wintering sites are often in six or even seven figures.

38 Russki Zavarot Peninsula, Nenets Just one of many marshy tundra areas of the Russian Arctic, liberally sprinkled with lakes, and bordering tidal mudflats. Up to 2000 pairs of Whooper and Bewick's Swans breed here and over 10,000 gather for the late-summer moult. Tens of thousands of geese and ducks also occur, especially prior to the autumn migration.

39 Kandalakshskaya Bay, Murmansk Nearly 10,000 pairs of Common Eiders breed on the myriad small islands in this bay. They are joined by up to 10,000 Goldeneyes during the post-breeding moult.

40 Onega Bay, White Sea Swans and geese by the hundreds of thousands gather on the mudflats and coastal marshes on migration, especially in the autumn, including Whooper and Bewick's Swans and Barnacle and Brent Geese.

41 North-east Caspian Sea and Volga Delta Huge numbers of waterbirds breed here, including, among the wildfowl, 3000 pairs of Mute Swans, 10,000 pairs of Greylag Geese and 8000 pairs of Pochard. These totals are dwarfed by the wintering hordes, which include a quarter of a million Mute Swans and a million ducks, mainly Pintail, Tufted Duck, Red-breasted Merganser and Smew.

42 Lake Manych-Gudilo This large shallow lake is the autumn stopping place for up to 25,000 Red-breasted Geese, 45,000 White-fronted Geese and 5000 Lesser White-fronted Geese. Over 40,000 Shelduck and other duck species moult here.

43 Primorsko-Akhtarsk salt lakes Situated on the east side of the Sea of Azov, these natural salt lakes are one of the key duck moulting sites in Eurasia, with counts of up to a million birds. Several hundred thousand stay through the winter.

Estonia

The Gulf of Finland, between Estonia and Finland, acts as a massive guideline for birds migrating between north-west Europe and Russia. Literally millions of birds pass through in spring and autumn. While their stopovers may be brief, the importance of the sites they use cannot be overestimated.

44 Matsalu Bay Over a million seaducks, mainly Longtails and scoters, have been counted in spring. Many thousands of Whooper and Bewick's Swans and Bean, White-fronted, Greylag and Barnacle Geese also pass through in spring and autumn, together with 30,000–40,000 dabbling ducks.

Latvia

Although off the main migration route, Latvia has many wetlands that provide breeding habitat for wildfowl.

45 Lake Engure Over 1000 pairs of Pochard and 250 pairs of Tufted Duck breed at this shallow lake. At least 13,000 ducks gather during the post-breeding moult.

Ukraine

The southern part of this country, bordering the Black Sea and the Sea of Azov, is winter home to very large numbers of wildfowl of many species.

46 Danube Delta and Yagorlytski and Tendra Bays The Russian part of the Danube Delta and adjacent sea bays are important for wintering White-fronted Geese and Mute Swans (several thousands of each) but principally as the wintering area for up to a quarter of a million Mallard.

Azerbaijan

Just a small part of this country lies within the Western Palearctic, along the north shore of the Caspian Sea, which attracts great numbers of wintering wildfowl.

47 Kirov Bay, Caspian Sea Shallow water backed by marshes and agricultural land attract up to half a million diving ducks and 200,000 dabbling ducks. Over 10,000 Lesser White-fronted Geese occur here, together with 40,000 Whitefronts and Greylags.

Poland

There are over 1000 lakes in Poland, which, together with extensive marshes and bogs, attract good numbers of nesting and passage wildfowl. Most lakes freeze in winter, but coastal lagoons on the Baltic stay open and are important for wintering birds.

48 Vistula Lagoon A brackish coastal lagoon in eastern Poland at which over 1000 Mute Swans moult, and where nearly 10,000 Pochard and Tufted Duck stop over in spring and autumn.

49 Szczecin Bay This large estuary holds wintering seaducks, including 6000 Goldeneye, 2000 Smew and 10,000 Goosanders. Over 10,000 each of Tufted Duck and Goldeneye are present on autumn passage.

50 Odra valley The water meadows and marshes up the River Odra from Szczecin Bay attract many thousands of Bean, White-fronted and Greylag Geese on spring and autumn passage. Lakes in the area hold 30,000–40,000 wintering ducks, mainly Tufted, Goldeneye and Goosander.

51 Słońsk Reserve The wet pastures and marshes of this river floodplain can hold over 30,000 Bean Geese in autumn, while the flooded areas attract over 30,000 ducks of several species in spring and twice that number in the autumn. Nearly 50,000 geese and the same number of ducks stay through there in mild winters.

*Ducks will mob land predators such as foxes from the safety of the water,
following them and keeping and eye on them. They will also mob dogs, which
are used to attract ducks into special traps called decoys.*

Czech Republic

Fish-ponds have compensated for some
drainage of natural wetlands. There
are a few concentrations of wintering
wildfowl, but breeding numbers are
mostly small and scattered.

52 Lednice and Pohořelice ponds
These large ponds with their associated
reedbeds act as roosting places for
5000–7000 each of Bean and Greylag
Geese on passage. Up to 2000 Shoveler
and 300 Red-crested Pochard have
been counted there.

53 Nový Mlyny middle reservoir
This flood-control reservoir is an
important migration stopover for up to
20,000 Bean Geese, 8000 Greylags and
20,000 Mallard. Several thousand
Bean Geese stay in mild winters.

Slovakia

The same comments regarding
wetlands apply as for the Czech
Republic. However, there are still
extensive wetlands along the banks of
the Danube.

**54 Danube flood-plain, near
Bratislava** This extensive area has lately
been much modified by construction of
a large canal but has recently held up

to 20,000 Bean and Greylag Geese and 25,000 Mallard on passage, with smaller numbers wintering.

Hungary

Extensive areas of marsh remain in the lowland plain and these, together with the many fish-ponds, attract passage and wintering ducks. Geese roost on the wetlands and feed out in the surrounding farmland.

55 Hortobágy This area provides marshes, fish-ponds, reedbeds and salt lakes set in agricultural land. Several thousand grey geese (Bean, Whitefront, Greylag) occur in autumn. Mallard have peaked at over 50,000.

56 Kis-Balaton An extensive freshwater marsh which, together with a reservoir, is very important in both spring and autumn. Up to 10,000 Bean Geese occur here, while 10,000 Pochard have been counted in the spring, as well as 1000 Goldeneye.

Austria

Almost the only fertile wetlands of any size in this mountainous country are in the east. They are used by breeding, passage and wintering wildfowl.

Three male Red-crested Pochard (lower) display to a female. A male's most noticeable feature is his red head. In courtship he raises the feathers into a bushy crest to make it more conspicuous and then swims in front of the female turning his head from side to side, showing it off and also the black nape patch which becomes more obvious when the head feathers are erected (see pages 96–8).

57 Neusiedler See This large, but very shallow, salt lake is bounded by enormous reedbeds, up to 6 km wide. Up to 300 pairs of Greylag breed here, as do Ferruginous Ducks. Over 2000 each of Gadwall and Shoveler and 700 Teal occur in autumn.

58 Seewinkel This area is similar in character to the Hortobágy of Hungary, and here, too, Bean, White-fronted and Greylag Geese occur on passage, totalling up to 35,000 birds. Duck numbers and species are much the same as those on Neusiedler See.

Germany

There are many good coastal areas for wildfowl in both the North Sea and the Baltic. Some of the larger complexes of inland lakes in the former East Germany hold considerable numbers of diving ducks, as do those in the Baden-Wurttemberg and Bavaria regions of the former West Germany.

59 Rügen/Hiddensee These shallow coastal lagoons, dotted with islands, are used on autumn migration by 20,000 each of Greylag and White-fronted Geese as well as by thousands of Teal, Tufted Duck and Goldeneye, many of which stay for the winter along with 2000 Goosanders and 500 Smew.

60 Greifswalder Bay Similar in many respects to the previous site, the bay attracts much larger numbers of passage birds, including up to 70,000 White-fronted Geese, 10,000 Greylags, 20,000 Wigeon, 10,000 Teal, 30,000 Scaup and 50,000 Long-tailed Ducks. Some of these stay for the winter and are joined by up to 8000 Goosanders.

61 Galenbecker See and Putzarer See These two freshwater lakes have small numbers of breeding Gadwall, Garganey and Red-crested Pochard but are important principally for passage ducks, especially 3000 Gadwall, 1500 each of Teal and Shoveler and 3500 Pochard. Up to 20,000 each of Greylag and White-fronted Geese roost here in spring and autumn and feed in the surrounding meadows.

62 Gülper See and Schollener See The valley of the River Haller contains extensive wet meadows together with these two lakes. Up to 200 pairs of Greylags breed, while over 6000 occur in autumn. Much more numerous, though, are the Bean Geese (over 50,000 on autumn passage) and White-fronted Geese (over 30,000). Some hundreds of Whooper and Bewick's Swans occur in spring.

63 Baltic coast, Schleswig-Holstein Large numbers of diving ducks and seaducks occur along this coast and in some of the fjords and bays. Several tens of thousands of Common Eiders, Scaup and Tufted Ducks occur on autumn passage, staying on in mild winters.

64 North and East Friesian Wadden Sea These two huge areas along the west coast of Schleswig-Holstein share many of the same birds with the Danish section of the Wadden Sea, with counts of over 80,000 Dark-bellied Brent Geese, 100,000 Shelducks (moulting), 150,000 Wigeon and in excess of 10,000 each of Mallard, Teal and Pintail. Common Eiders are also abundant, with counts totalling over 100,000. The highest numbers occur during the autumn.

65 Niederrhein Nearly 200,000 geese, mainly Bean and White-fronted, winter along the river valley in this district, using floodwaters and agricultural land.

66 Auenheim to Greffern, River Rhine This is just one of a number of localities along the Rhine where a dam has produced a large lake which, together with adjacent pools and tributaries, attracts large numbers of wintering wildfowl. Mallard are typically most numerous, here about 18,000, while Pochard and Tufted Duck can be nearly as plentiful.

67 Untersee The German, north-eastern, part of Lake Constance has shallow bays and reedbeds with breeding Red-crested Pochard and some tens of thousands of wintering Tufted Duck and Pochard.

Switzerland

The large lakes in this otherwise almost completely mountainous country provide good wintering sites for substantial numbers of ducks.

68 Untersee or Bodensee (Lake Constance) Like the German, north-eastern side of this lake, the Swiss, south-western, part has reedbeds, and areas of exposed mud when the water level drops sufficiently, Up to 100,000 ducks can be found over the whole lake at this time, with Tufted Duck and Pochard among the commonest.

A pair of Goldeneye complete their copulation. The male retains his hold on her neck feathers while both birds rotate in tight circles before separating and then bathing and preening (see page 103).

A Red-breasted Goose dozing on one leg. Standing on one leg is comfortable, and in a strong wind enables the bird to sway to and fro in gusts (see page 123).

The Netherlands

Approximately 10,000 swans, 700,000 geese and nearly a million ducks winter in this one, comparatively small country. Despite intensive farming and a very high density of humans, there are many large and important wetlands, only a very small selection of which can be given here.

69 Waddenzee The Dutch part of the Wadden Sea is just as important as its German and Danish sections, with over 50,000 each of Barnacle and Brent Geese, Shelduck and Wigeon, over 100,000 Common Eiders, and tens of thousands of Teal, Mallard, Scaup and Common Scoter.

70 Lauwersmeer Several hundred pairs of Shelduck, Gadwall and Shoveler, together with about 50 pairs of Garganey, nest around this freshwater lake, formerly an estuary. Up to 4000 Bewick's Swans, 35,000 Barnacle Geese and 40,000 Wigeon occur on passage.

71 IJsselmeer The shallow waters of this huge lake hold tremendous concentrations of diving ducks and seaducks, including 50,000 Pochard, over 100,000 Tufted Duck, 10,000 Goldeneye, up to 9000 Smew, and nearly 10,000 each of Red-breasted Merganser and Goosander.

72 Oostvaardersplassen and Lepelaarsplassen When the South

141

Flevoland Polder was created to reclaim farmland, these two areas of lakes and reedbeds were kept as conservation areas. Over 50,000 each of White-fronted and Greylag Geese winter, with about 30,000 of the latter gathering to moult in the late summer. Wintering ducks include Gadwall (1500), Teal (10,000), Mallard (50,000), Pintail (25,000), Shoveler (5000), Tufted Duck (5000), Smew (up to 10,000) and Goosander (5000).

73 Grevelingen One of a number of wetlands in south-west Netherlands formed by damming estuaries. They typically include extensive mudflats and reedbeds, holding, in this case, over 30,000 Mallard, 4500 Teal, 20,000 Wigeon and some thousands of Barnacle and Brent Geese.

Belgium

There are many small wetlands in Belgium but only a few of major importance.

74 Coastal polders at Damme and Zwin Wintering geese in this area exceed 50,000 (mainly White-fronted, with some Bean and Pink-footed). Wigeon (up to 20,000) are the most numerous duck.

France

Major wetlands include the extensive estuaries along the Atlantic coast, some inland lakes and marshes, and the very important coastal lagoons and marshes of the Mediterranean. All of these hold good numbers of wintering wildfowl,

although hunting pressure is high in some areas. Numbers of breeding wildfowl are mostly small.

75 Golfe du Morbihan This is the most important estuarine complex on the eastern Atlantic coast. Up to 20,000 Dark-bellied Brent Geese winter, together with 2500 Shelduck, up to 25,000 Wigeon, 4000 Teal, 3500 Pintail and 1500 Red-breasted Mergansers.

76 Baie de l'Aiguillon A complex of estuaries and wet meadows with large numbers of wintering Mallard (20,000), Teal (20,000), Wigeon (15,000), Pintail (6000), Shoveler (5000) and Common Scoter (10,000).

77 Camargue Perhaps better known for its Flamingos and other waterbirds, the Camargue nevertheless holds very large numbers of wintering ducks, including up to 12,000 Gadwall, 50,000 Teal, 20,000 Wigeon, 40,000 Mallard, 6000 Pintail, 16,000 Shoveler, 5500 Red-crested Pochard, 13,000 Pochard and 7500 Tufted Duck.

A family party of Barnacle Geese feeding on the tundra. The parents look after the goslings throughout their first year. The male in particular spends more time on guard checking for danger while the goslings and also the female, which needs to build up its body reserves after egg-laying and incubation, can feed undisturbed (see page 67).

SOUTHERN EUROPE AND TURKEY

Although there are a few breeding species here at the north of their range, including Ruddy Shelduck, Marbled Duck and White-headed Duck, the major importance of this region for wildfowl is as a mild wintering area for birds coming from further north. The irregular hard winters of north-west Europe often send large numbers of extra birds south towards the Mediterranean for short periods.

Portugal

There are few wetlands of any size in Portugal, although some of the coastal lagoons and estuaries hold reasonable numbers of wintering wildfowl.

78 Tejo Estuary The large expanses of mudflats and saltings attract several hundred wintering Greylag Geese, over 6000 Teal and 1500 Shoveler.

Spain

The most important Spanish wetlands are inland lakes in the south and estuaries and lagoons along the Mediterranean coast. Small breeding populations of White-headed Duck and Marbled Duck are at the western edge of their ranges here.

79 Marismas del Guadalquivir These famous marshes at the mouth of the River Guadalquivir, although much drained and further threatened, hold up to 175 breeding pairs of Marbled Duck. The peak winter counts of Greylag Geese (up to 70,000), Gadwall (8500), Teal (125,000), Pintail (40,000), Shoveler (85,000) and Red-crested Pochard (5000) attest to its international importance.

80 Albufera de Valencia A large coastal freshwater lagoon holding, at peak, over 24,000 Shoveler and 12,000 Red-crested Pochard.

81 Ebro Delta About 1500 pairs of Red-crested Pochard breed in this complex of estuarine lagoons, saltings, sea bays and paddyfields. Wintering duck total 70,000, principally Wigeon, Teal, Mallard and Shoveler.

Italy

The most important wetlands are the estuaries and lagoons of the north Adriatic coast. Elsewhere, and especially inland, wetlands are mostly small and many are subject to heavy hunting pressure.

82 Po Delta This very large delta has winter peaks of 10,000 Wigeon, 4000 Shoveler and 400 Goldeneye.

83 Laguna di Venezia Several thousand ducks winter here, including up to 3500 Mallard, 2000 Teal and 2500 Pochard.

84 Laguna di Grado e Marano A complex of estuary and tidal lagoon holding up to 5000 Bean, White-fronted and Greylag Geese, 8000 Wigeon, 6000 Teal, 10,000 Mallard and over 7000 Goldeneye.

Two male Goldeneye display vigorously to a female. The male at the top of the picture has stretched his neck to the utmost and is holding his head up in the 'bowsprit' display. The lower male has thrown his head right over on to his back. He is uttering a distinctive 'zeee-ZEEE' call before bringing his head sharply forward again (see page 102).

A Pochard leaps into the air before diving. This characteristic movement of diving ducks, Pochard, Tufted Duck, Scaup, etc., gives extra impetus in the dive, helping them go down further than if they pushed off from the surface (see page 29).

Slovenia

Wetlands are comparatively scarce in Slovenia, although floods along river valleys provide some good habitat.

85 River Drava valley near Maribor This is one of the few sites for geese, with 1500 Bean Geese wintering, together with up to 13,000 Mallard, 3000 Teal and 1000 Goldeneye.

Croatia

Floodplains and fish-ponds form most wetlands: coastal wetlands are few.

86 Fish-ponds in the Pokupsko Depression This area is important for breeding and wintering Ferruginous Duck, with up to 80 pairs at one pond complex and perhaps 5000 in winter.

87 Kopački rit The floodplain of the Danube and Drava attracts large numbers of Bean Geese and Mallard, both peaking at 50,000 on autumn passage, staying on in mild winters. Up to 200 pairs of Ferruginous Duck have been reported as breeding here.

Macedonia

A few large lakes provide wintering habitat for wildfowl.

88 Lake Ohrid This lake attracts diving ducks, with 1300 Red-crested Pochard, 7000 Pochard and 2000 Tufted Duck counted in one winter.

Greece

The most important wetlands in Greece are deltas and estuarine complexes. A few large lakes also hold wintering wildfowl.

89 Évros Delta A small number of pairs of Ruddy Shelduck and about twenty pairs of Ferruginous Duck breed, but the main importance of this complex of marsh, lagoons, saltpans and river is for wintering ducks, in particular 35,000 Teal, 36,000 Pintail and 15,000 Wigeon.

90 Porto Lágo The freshwater lakes and brackish lagoons in this area hold up to 400 White-headed Duck in winter, as well as several thousands of Teal, Pintail, Shoveler and Pochard. White-fronted, Lesser White-fronted and Greylag Geese all reside here during winter.

91 Lake Kerkini This reservoir holds breeding Greylag Goose and Ferruginous Duck and attracts as many as 40,000 Teal and 30,000 Mallard in winter.

92 Gulf of Amvrakia The deltas of the Rivers Loúros and Árakhthos provide excellent wetland habitat for up to 150,000 ducks, principally Wigeon, Teal, Pintail and Pochard.

93 Mesolóngi Lagoons Coastal marshes and pools used by up to

The Shoveler is the most highly adapted of the dabbling ducks. Its massive bill broadens towards the tip and so increases the volume of water which the bird can sieve. Its lamellae are finer and more numerous than other species, enabling it to feed on tinier seeds and invertebrates (see page 15).

15,000 wintering Wigeon and some 20,000 Pochard.

Romania

By far the most important wetlands are associated with the River Danube, both along its length and, in particular, at its delta. Other Black Sea coastal areas are also important.

94 Danube Delta Although much threatened by continuing development, this large area of river channels, lakes and vast reedbeds is still of prime importance. Breeding wildfowl include 500 pairs of Mute Swans and possibly White-headed Duck. At least 100,000 White-fronted Geese and 12,000–25,000 Red-breasted Geese winter here, feeding on the surrounding agricultural land. Ducks are also very numerous, with up to 150,000 Teal, 200,000 Mallard, 40,000 Shoveler, 32,000 Red-crested Pochard, 13,000 Ferruginous Duck and nearly a million Pochard, to serve as just some indication of their abundance.

Bulgaria

The most important wetlands are concentrated along the Danube and also the Black Sea coast.

95 Lakes Sabla-Ezeretz This complex of lakes has held up to 17,000 Red-breasted Geese as well as 30,000 Whitefronts. Ducks are also numerous, with peak counts of Mallard in excess of 66,000.

Turkey

Enormous numbers of wildfowl pass through Turkey or winter on its wetlands, which include several huge lakes, many at considerable altitude, as well as coastal sites such as estuaries. Only a handful of them can be described here.

96 Kizilirmak Delta Situated on the Black Sea coast, this delta holds up to 5000 wintering Greylag Geese and up to 70,000 ducks, especially Mallard, Teal, Pintail and Shoveler.

97 Ereğli Sazliği A very large lake with extensive reedbeds, which has breeding Ruddy Shelduck, Marbled Duck and White-headed Duck. As many as 10,000 geese and 30,000 ducks occur on passage and during winter, among which the most notable are up to 8000 Ruddy Shelducks.

98 Sultan Marshes This huge plain with saltpans and brackish marshes attracts some breeding wildfowl but enormous numbers on passage and in winter. Over half a million Teal have been counted here, as well as 11,000 Ruddy Shelducks, 9000 Shoveler, 17,000 Red-crested Pochard and 40,000 Pochard.

99 Cukurova A complex of river deltas and lakes with up to 100 breeding pairs of Marbled Duck. Over a quarter of a million Teal have been estimated here in mid-winter together with many thousands of Wigeon, Garganey, Pintail, Shoveler and Pochard.

Sleeping Whooper Swans (above left) *curl their neck over their body and rest the head on the back, the bill tip usually tucked into the feathers. The short-necked Wigeon* (below left) *turns its head towards its tail and tucks the whole bill under the scapulars, the long feathers at the inner edge of the wing (see page 123).*

A newly hatched Mallard duckling (lower). The downy plumage is still wet and spiky and it will take an hour or two to dry out under the soft warmth of the mother's belly feathers. Only when this has happened (upper) will the down provide the duckling with an insulating and waterproof covering (see page 108).

NORTH AFRICA AND THE MIDDLE EAST

The south side of the Mediterranean has small numbers of breeding birds but large numbers of wintering ducks, especially the dabbling species. Many wetlands are of a temporary nature, dependent upon erratic winter rains.

Morocco

Most of Morocco's wetlands are on the Atlantic or Mediterranean coasts, mainly river estuaries and brackish lagoons. Some of the lakes in the Atlas mountains also attract passage and wintering ducks, as do temporary floods which appear after winter rains.

100 Merja Zerga This large brackish lagoon holds up to 50,000 wintering ducks, mainly Wigeon, but also Teal, Pintail and Garganey.

Algeria

Coastal lagoons and marshes are important for wildfowl; both fresh and salt lakes occur, some subject to temporary flooding. Inland marshes

150

and mountain lakes are also thought to be good wildfowl wintering sites.

101 El Kala complex Five sites, both fresh and salt, close to the coast, have held nearly 200,000 wildfowl in winter, with Wigeon predominating but also 20,000–30,000 each of Tufted Duck and Pochard. Up to 5000 Greylags occur at one of the sites.

Tunisia

Several shallow freshwater lakes and saltpans provide excellent wintering habitat for wildfowl, although some are subject to drainage or damming proposals and others depend on seasonal rainfall.

102 Lake Ichkeul Probably the most important wetland in North Africa, this large shallow lake attracts over 10,000 Greylag Geese and up to 150,000 ducks, especially Wigeon and Pochard, and Teal and Shoveler. White-headed Duck are regular in small numbers.

103 Sebkhet El-Kelbia Over a quarter of a million ducks have been counted here in wet winters, although in dry years numbers are much smaller. Wigeon, Pintail, Shoveler and Pochard are all numerous.

Libya

Detailed information on wetlands in this country is limited, as is access.

Several potentially important areas occur along the Mediterranean coast and at some of the temporary salt lakes inland.

Egypt

The most important wetlands for wildfowl are close to the Mediterranean coast.

104 Lake Burullus This huge shallow coastal wetland has held very large numbers of Wigeon and Gadwall, but is probably most notable for the enormous totals of Shoveler that have been counted there, in excess of 60,000.

105 Nile Delta Regular and accurate information is hard to come by, but, despite development and much disturbance, the area can still be regarded as of prime importance for many wintering ducks, especially dabbling species.

Israel

Many former marshy areas have been drained. Fish-ponds in some areas have proved attractive to small numbers of wildfowl.

106 Hula Nature Reserve A remnant of once very extensive marshes in the north of the country. Marbled Duck breeds, and modest numbers of several species of duck pass through on passage or stay for the winter.

BIBLIOGRAPHY

Alison, R., 'Breeding biology and behaviour of the Oldsquaw', *Ornithol. Monogr.* 18 (1975)

Amat, J.A., 'Food usurpation by waterfowl and waders', *Wildfowl* 41 (1990), 107–116

Anderson, B.W., Reeder, M.G., and Timken, R.L., 'Notes on the feeding behavior of the Common Merganser', *Condor* 76 (1974), 472–6

Birkhead, M., and Perrins, C., *The Mute Swan*, Croom Helm, London, 1986

Black, J.M., 'Pre-flight signalling in swans: a mechanism for group cohension and flock formation', *Ethology*, 79 (1988), 143–57

Black, J.M. and Owen, M., 'Parent-offspring relationships in wintering Barnacle Geese', *Anim. Behav.*, 37 (1989), 187–98

Boyd, H., 'On encounters between wild White-fronted Geese in winter flocks', *Behaviour* 5 (1953), 85–129

Boyd, H., and Fox, A.D., 'Sexual activity of Pink-footed Geese at a staging area in Iceland', *Wildfowl* 43 (1992), 117–20

Bregnballe, T., and Madsen, J., 'Post-hatching behaviour of Light-bellied Brent Geese', *Wildfowl* 41 (1990), 27–34

Cramp, S., and Simmons, K.E.L., *The Birds of the Western Palearctic*, Volume I, Oxford University Press, Oxford, 1977

Draulans, D., 'Foraging and size selection of mussels by Tufted Duck', *J. Anim. Ecol.* 51 (1982), 943–56

Ebbinge, B., Canters, K., and Drent, R., 'Foraging routines and estimated daily food intake in Barnacle Geese wintering in the northern Netherlands', *Wildfowl* 26 (1975), 5–19

Gauthier, G., 'Territorial behaviour, forced copulations and mixed reproductive strategy in ducks', *Wildfowl* 39 (1988), 102–14

Gillham, E., *Tufted Ducks in a Royal Park*, Eric Gillham, Kent, 1987

Goldburn, S.F., 'Mate guarding in the Mallard', *Ornis Scand.* 15 (1984), 261–5

Grimmett, R.F.A., and Jones, T.A., *Important Bird Areas in Europe*, ICBP, Cambridge, 1989

Hill, D.A., 'Factors affecting nest success in Mallard and Tufted Duck', *Ornis Scand.* 15 (1984), 115–22

Johnsgard, P.A., *The Handbook of Waterfowl Behavior*, Cornell University Press, Ithaca, 1965

Johnson, I.P., and Sibley, R.M., 'Mate protection in pre-nesting Canada Geese', *Wildfowl* 41 (1990), 38–42

Lazarus, J., and Inglis, I.R., 'The breeding behaviour of the Pink-footed Goose: parental care and vigilant behaviour during the fledging period', *Behaviour* 65 (1978), 62–88

Lissaman, P.B.S., and Shollenberg, C.A., 'Formation flight of birds', *Science* 168 (1970), 1003–5

McKinney, F., 'Spacing and chasing in breeding ducks', *Wildfowl Trust Ann. Rep.* 16 (1965), 108–21

Miles, H., and Salisbury, M., *Kingdom of the Ice Bear*, BBC Books, London, 1985

Nielsen, S., *Mallards*, Swan Hill Press, Shrewsbury, 1992

Ogilvie, M.A., *The Ducks of Britain and Europe*, Poyser, Berkhamstead, 1975

Ogilvie, M.A., *Wild Geese*, Poyser, Berkhamstead, 1978

Ogilvie, M.A., *Birdwatching on inland fresh waters*, Severn House, London, 1981

Owen, M., *Wild Geese of the world*, Batsford, London, 1980

Owen, M., Atkinson-Willes, G.L., and Salmon, D.G., *Wildfowl in Great Britain*, 2nd edition, Cambridge University Press, Cambridge, 1986

Patterson, I.J., *The Shelduck – a study in behavioural ecology*, Cambridge University Press, Cambridge, 1982

Pöysä, H., 'Costs and benefits of group foraging in the Teal', *Behaviour* 103 (1987), 123–40

Rees, E.C., 'Bewick's swans: their feeding ecology and coexistence with other grazing Anatidae', *J. Appl. Ecol.* 27 (1990), 939–51

Reynolds, P., 'Observations on the time budget and diving ecology of Long-tailed Ducks in Eqalungmuit Nunaat, West Greenland', *Wildfowl* 38 (1987), 55–62

Salomonsen, F., 'The moult migration', *Wildfowl* 19 (1968), 5–24

Schenkeveld, L.E., and Ydenberg, R.C., 'Synchronous diving by Surf Scoters', *Can. J. Zool.* 63 (1985), 2516–9

Scott, P., and the Wildfowl Trust, *The Swans*, Michael Joseph, London, 1972

Thomas, G.J., 'Autumn and winter feeding ecology of waterfowl at the Ouse Washes, England', *J. Zool. Lond.* 197 (1982), 131–72

Weller, M.W. (Ed.), *Waterfowl in Winter*, University of Minnesota Press, Minneapolis, 1988

Williams, T.C., Klonowski, T.J., and Berkeley, P., 'Angle of Canada Goose V flight formation measured by radar', *Auk* 93 (1976), 554–9

Ydenberg, R.C., and Prins, H.H., 'Spring grazing and manipulation of food quality by Barnacle Geese', *J. Appl. Ecol.* 18 (1981), 443–53

Scientific Names

All bird species mentioned in the text are listed below, with their scientific name, in systematic order.

divers	*Gavia*
grebes	Podicipedidae
petrels and shearwaters	Procellariiformes
Flamingo	*Phoenicopterus ruber*

ANSERIFORMES
Anatidae

Mute Swan	*Cygnus olor*
Bewick's Swan	*C. columbianus bewickii*
Whooper Swan	*C. cygnus*
Bean Goose	*Anser fabalis*
Pink-footed Goose	*A. brachyrhynchus*
White-fronted Goose	*A. albifrons*
Greenland White-fronted Goose	*A. a. flavirostris*
Lesser White-fronted Goose	*A. erythropus*
Greylag Goose	*A. anser*
Snow Goose	*A. caerulescens*
Canada Goose	*Branta canadensis*
Barnacle Goose	*B. leucopsis*
Brent Goose	*B. bernicla*
Dark-bellied Brent Goose	*B. b. bernicla*
Light-bellied Brent Goose	*B. b. hrota*
Red-breasted Goose	*B. ruficollis*
Egyptian Goose	*Alopochen aegyptiacus*
Ruddy Shelduck	*Tadorna ferruginea*
Shelduck	*T. tadorna*
Wood Duck	*Aix sponsa*
Mandarin Duck	*A. galericulata*
Wigeon	*Anas penelope*
American Wigeon	*A. americana*
Gadwall	*A. strepera*
Baikal Teal	*A. formosa*
Teal	*A. crecca*
Green-winged Teal	*A. c. carolinensis*
Mallard	*A. platyrhynchos*
Black Duck	*A rubripes*
Pintail	*A. acuta*

Garganey	*A. querquedula*
Blue-winged Teal	*A. discors*
Shoveler	*A. clypeata*
Marbled Duck	*Marmaronetta angustirostris*
Red-crested Pochard	*Netta rufina*
Pochard	*Aythya ferina*
Ring-necked Duck	*A. collaris*
Ferruginous Duck	*A. nyroca*
Tufted Duck	*A. fuligula*
Scaup	*A. marila*
Lesser Scaup	*A. affinis*
Common Eider	*Somateria mollissima*
King Eider	*S. spectabilis*
Steller's Eider	*Polysticta stelleri*
Harlequin Duck	*Histrionicus histrionicus*
Long-tailed Duck	*Clangula hyemalis*
Common Scoter	*Melanitta nigra*
Surf Scoter	*M. perspicillata*
Velvet Scoter	*M. fusca*
Bufflehead	*Bucephala albeola*
Barrow's Goldeneye	*B. islandica*
Goldeneye	*B. clangula*
Hooded Merganser	*Mergus cucullatus*
Smew	*M. albellus*
Red-breasted Merganser	*M. serrator*
Goosander	*M. merganser*
Ruddy Duck	*Oxyura jamaicensis*
White-headed Duck	*O. leucocephala*
Peregrine	*Falco peregrinus*
rails	Rallidae
Coot	*Fulica atra*
cranes	Gruidae
Herring Gull	*Larus argentatus*
Great Black-backed Gull	*L. marinus*
Robin	*Erithacus rubecula*
babblers	Timaliidae
crows	Corvidae
Starling	*Sturnus vulgaris*

INDEX

References in *italics* are to illustrations.